Advance Praise for
A Future So Bright

Kate O'Neill has stumbled upon an insight that is incredibly important for those of us who haven't given up on the future. She weaves her expertise and direct experience working with tech companies with an infectious optimism, helping us see our role in solving some of our most important problems. A Future So Bright helps us understand that we'll get the kind of disruption we're willing to fight for.

— *Caleb Gardner, founding partner at 18 Coffees, and former digital director at OFA (BarackObama.com)*

So much of the future is painted in polarized views. Kate O'Neill's fresh take bridges the gap and lays the foundation for embracing technology, empathy and opportunity as we speed towards a hopeful future.

— *Chris Mattmann, Chief Technology and Innovation Officer at NASA JPL, Professor, Author*

A breath of fresh air in what often feels like times of desperation, Kate O'Neill delivers us the brighter future vision we crave and the strategy we need to bring it to life. This isn't just hope for a better future, this is determined optimism with a game plan.

— *Olivia Gambelin, AI ethicist and founder of Ethical Intelligence*

Praise for
Tech Humanist

For the past two decades, the Computer History Museum has chronicled the amazing rise of the technology which just in our lifetime has become the most powerful agent of change the world has ever known. While the stories of creativity, invention, innovation, and impact are fascinating, what all this means for the future and humanity is what we are poised to take on now as an institution. And nowhere has this become more clear to me and my colleagues here at the museum than in reading Kate O'Neill's blog post entitled "The Tech Humanist Manifesto." The idea that we need to develop and embed in all future technologies the very best of ourselves and our ethics and ultimately have the goal of those emerging technologies to make us better humans has resonated deeply into our own plans of what we will present, discuss, and debate going forward.

After reading the manifesto, my initial thoughts were "Kate should write a book on this." Which I am very happy that she has done, and now her humor, excellent insights, and heartfelt philosophy can reach the leaders and influencers throughout the world. And the rest of us too.

— *Gary Matsushita, Vice President, Computer History Museum*

Praise for
Pixels and Place

Kate O'Neill's Pixels and Place is a must read for those of us fascinated by the tidal shift taking place around us in the way we envision the world and our experiences within it.

— *Mitch Lowe, startup advisor, CEO of MoviePass, former president of RedBox, and a founding executive of Netflix*

A
FUTURE
SO
BRIGHT

How **Strategic Optimism** and Meaningful Innovation
Can Restore Our Humanity and **Save the World**

by
KATE O'NEILL

Copyright © 2021 by Kate O'Neill
First Edition, 2021

Published in the United States of America

ISBN-13: 978-1-7371878-0-6

Dedication

To young activists all around the world who will not give up the bright future without a fight.

A note on my use of the generic gender-neutral singular pronoun "they"

Throughout this book, as I describe scenarios involving unspecified actors, instead of the arbitrary use of a single gendered pronoun in generic use, whether "he" or "she," instead of the clunky "he/she" or wordy "he or she," and instead of painstakingly alternating between the uses of gendered pronouns, I have adopted the use of the singular "they." It was the American Dialect Society's 2015 word of the year, and it reflects a trend toward more inclusive language, and, hopefully, a more inclusive society.

"The future is no more uncertain than the present."
— Walt Whitman

**"My optimism wears heavy boots
and is loud."
— Henry Rollins**

INTRODUCTION:

The brighter future needs you to build it.

WE HUMANS HERE ON PLANET EARTH in the early part of the twenty-first century face dramatic and unprecedented change. In fact, we are dealing with several overlapping vectors of change and complexity:

- The planet's average temperatures are rising, causing accelerating climate-related catastrophes and unpredictable weather patterns, as well as impacts on human migration, political unrest, and all of life on earth

- We've begun to introduce increasingly intelligent automation, and its impact on the future of human work and jobs is unclear

- Geopolitics are in upheaval, resulting in a pull toward populist authoritarianism and fascism

- Long-overdue reckonings with racial justice issues, histories of slavery and colonialism, and other local and global social justice issues demand our attention

- Misinformation and disinformation about critically important topics are on the rise in an increasingly polarized media landscape and an increasingly algorithmically-optimized content ecosystem that reinforces polarization and extremism

- Novel diseases are spreading rapidly in an increasingly global community, as demonstrated by COVID-19 and its variants

Not all of the change on that list is bad or without opportunity, but most of it is happening so rapidly—even exponentially—that the future seems more complicated than ever to predict and plan for. What's more, it all connects. It's impossible to consider the COVID-19 pandemic, for example, without thinking about the societal inequities it laid bare: the disparate impacts on marginalized populations, the lack of access to vaccines in poorer countries, and so on. And how the rise of populist authoritarianism made public health information more challenging and turned emerging scientific consensus into hotly debated political issues that were contentiously partisan. Every piece of that is connected to everything else. To untangle one issue, we need to be willing to untangle all of them.

Now, take a deep breath.

That may all sound daunting. You may even think our situation is hopeless.

But the future isn't what we think.

The future is what we *do*—what we did, what we decided, what others decided for us. The future connects to the past. The past connects to the present. Everything touches and influences everything else. We each live in a future shaped by the actions and decisions we made—and everyone else made—at any and at every point in the past.

That means slipping toward dystopia *isn't* inevitable, and our fate isn't some vast unknowable thing. The future, after all, can be as simple as this next moment coming up, and then the one after that. The future is as much the moments you can see ahead of you and influence as the ones you can't easily foresee and can't imagine shaping. But we *do* shape them. The future is built on what we do.

Sure, you read those words. But to make sure we accept them and believe them, let's start small. Can you alter the next hour's likely course of events? Surely some of it. Maybe you take a break from your desk and drink a glass of water so you won't feel dehydrated. Guess what? You just demonstrated that you know how to alter the future. You used strategic means now to achieve better results later. Extend the thought a little further, and still a little further, and in the same way you decide not to spend all of your money today so you won't be too broke to buy a hamburger next Tuesday[1], we just as clearly have the chance to likewise make savvy decisions about what we do now that will leave the world with more options, more resources, and overall better outcomes in whatever time horizon of the future we think about. We have more control than we realize.

Our best bet for a bright future is to adopt a holistic, inclusive mindset about the challenges we face and how we face them. Because the decisions we make about any of them from moment to moment affect and create our collective future in real and direct ways.

The good news is that we are not powerless. We are, in fact, largely able to shape our own destinies, even in the face of dramatic and unprecedented change —with optimism.

Yes, with *optimism*.

And let's be honest. Optimism gets a bad rap.

That may be an unexpected stance during—as we've established—a time of climate catastrophe, a global pandemic, growing anxieties about artificial intelligence and automation, existential fears about the future of human work, geopolitical upheaval, and all the other what-have-you. But think of it: Hope and dedication gave us vaccines for a novel coronavirus in less than a year since it originated. More and more businesses are committing to reducing emissions, as well as other good-for-humanity programs. It's not all good news, of course, but the *opportunity* for good is undeniably always there. So for reasons I'll lay out here, the position I'm taking is clear-eyed, determined optimism with a commitment to follow-through, and it's the stance I hope you'll take alongside me before you're finished reading this book.

The problem with optimism has been that instead of wielding it as a powerful tool for envisioning and working toward the best outcomes, people roundly mock it as a folly of the naïve. Historically, optimism in literature and philosophy has been dismissed as unthinking, unserious, unintellectual. And when they aren't being ridiculed, optimists are scorned for willfully ignoring real harms.

---

[1] Do you remember "I'll gladly pay you Tuesday for a hamburger today" from the Popeye cartoons? I wonder if J. Wellington Wimpy would have been into the plant-based burger revolution, which is part of the brighter future of food we'll cover in Part Five.

3

But what about the advantages of looking at the bright side? A savvy approach to optimism can help us avoid the kind of failure that comes from not thinking about what might happen if things go better than we planned. And when it's used properly and paired with the right tools, as I'll explain in this book, optimism can actually help us acknowledge the whole truth of our circumstances, direct our focus, and align our efforts toward the best way forward.

Optimism doesn't have to be simple-minded, shortsighted, or unaccompanied by rationalism. So yes indeed, there is a way to harness the power of optimism so that it is as clear-eyed as possible, as strategic as possible, as inclusive as possible, as aligned with success as possible, as actionable as possible, and as achievable as possible. That is the only optimism worth having, and it is the approach this book lays out.

After all, you've just opened up a book about the future—an optimistic one at that!—so I'm going to assume you must not be *too* convinced of the futility of our prospects as a species. Still, you'd be well within your rights to wonder how on this rapidly-warming planet we can dare to take a hopeful view of everything that is uncertain and in a state of flux.

The best way—perhaps the *only* way—to build a bright future is to challenge ourselves to envision the best future possible for the most people *while at the same time* acknowledging the ways the future could go dark and working to prevent that from happening.

Looking at what can go right as well as what can go wrong is a key part of what I call the Strategic Optimism Model. I will introduce you to the idea of Strategic Optimism in the first part of this book. What this approach asks of us, in short, is to look at the whole picture, acknowledge the risks and the potential harms, and then actively work to mitigate them as we steer toward the most helpful, most meaningful outcomes.

The biggest obstacle in front of us? We've been taught to think about and talk about the future in too limited a way. Dystopia versus utopia? That's more than useless; it's dangerous. The falseness of that dichotomy (which we'll explore in Beyond "Dystopia versus Utopia"), the dismissal of utopia as impossible, and the resulting despair of being left to accept an ever-encroaching dystopia keeps us from focusing on and addressing what we *can* actively do every day to ensure tomorrow is better than today, and next year is better than this year. It's time to disrupt dystopia and give ourselves the freedom to imagine the bright future we really want to create.

To Recap

In short:

We are living through exponential changes and facing existential crises, and all we're equipped with are quaint sci-fi concepts of what the future once looked like. We have big challenges but even bigger opportunities. And the truth is, *you* direct the future.

We *all* make the future with every decision and action we choose today. So this is our chance to make the best decisions and create the brightest future. I'll walk us through how we can rethink how we do it.

In order to create the bright futures we envision, we will need:

• A better vocabulary for talking—and even for thinking—about the future

• A more holistic and inclusive framework for planning our way into the future

• Better tools—in fact, our Human Superpowers—for coping with the past and present as well as the uncertainty of the future

It's the moment of truth. We need radically hopeful, strategically bold leadership.

Will you help get us there?

Why this book, and why now?

"The best time to plant a tree was twenty years ago. The second best time is now." This is often cited as a Chinese proverb, but little evidence exists that it is a) Chinese or b) older than a few decades. However, there are other proverbs about trees which are more credibly of Chinese provenance and which have similarly wise messages, such as:

> "One generation plants the trees;
> another gets the shade."

And another:

> "It takes ten years to grow a tree
> and a hundred years to cultivate
> (a generation of) good people."

What these proverbs remind us is that we don't always have the luxury of doing the perfect things at the perfect time to produce perfect outcomes. We'd all love to have perfect foresight. If we knew back then what we should have done and when we should have done it, we'd have done it, right? Perhaps. But we don't have perfect foresight, and we don't live in a perfect world. So what matters is a mindset for continually recognizing what we need to do to make the world better and taking action to do it *now*.

Most of the books I have read about the future don't acknowledge one of the key shortcomings about most futurist discussions (see Beyond "Dystopia Versus Utopia"). Specifically, they actively subscribe to the false notion that the future is either dystopia or utopia—rather than a version of both/and—or something unknowable and frightening as opposed to the version of tomorrow we will create with today's actions. Most of what I've encountered doesn't emphasize our human agency in creating the bright future we would love to see. What I have tried to do differently with this book is to hold space for us to face the facts and confront the challenging realities head-on, but to do so with assuredness that we can beat the odds…if we do the work.

I believe in the power of today to shape tomorrow, and the opportunity that every challenge presents. I believe in the resilience of humanity and the resilience of nature, and I believe we haven't even begun to understand the power and harmony that can come from aligning our objectives with the earth. I believe we still have time—but we must act *very* quickly—to set in place a more meaningful future for humanity, and a more promising future for all life on this planet.

That's why this book exists, and that's why it needs to exist now. And that's also why I'm grateful you're reading it.

This is a toolkit for you.

A book's readers should come away feeling they have been recognized and understood, that they have been given some tools—a hammer, a match, some gasoline…whatever it takes to do the job they've been inspired to do. I do see you, and I have tools to offer you, although my hope is they will do less burning and more building.

It's possible, even likely, that the idea of the future gives you low-level anxiety. Perhaps its specter has terrified you at least once. You may lead teams and have people who look to you for management, for guidance, for a paycheck. You may have a family who looks to you for reassurance, for an example, for a paycheck.

It's hard to know what to tell them all. *Is* the future going to be all right? *Will* we be working? *Will* robots take over? *Will* the earth burn up? *Will* cities flood? *Will* politics divide us beyond repair?

These are big, frantic, existential questions, and they demand big, calm, existential answers—as well as small, simple, usable guidance. Yes, both. We need somewhere to put the big anxieties while we deal with the small stuff, and we need to do the small stuff in a way that moves it closer to the big stuff.

This book is for leaders. That's you.

The upshot, before I delve into anything else, is I have written this book for *you*, reader. For you.

I wrote this for leaders. Leaders of all kinds, really: business leaders, civic leaders, institutional leaders, world leaders.

And I believe leadership can come from anywhere, from anyone, at any time. In fact, we need leadership from all corners, from all communities, from all voices. And now more than ever, the least-heard voices are the ones we ought to listen to the most.

I've zoomed in especially close on a few specific kinds of leadership: business, technology, cities, and institutions. These focus areas have been partly shaped by my longstanding work around human experiences and where the

8

meaningful majority of those tend to play out; partly informed by where the biggest impact on the future consistently seemed to be in the research; and partly shaped by existing and ongoing dialogue I've had with decision-makers in these arenas, knowing they have key roles to play in bringing us forward into a brighter future.

For leaders of businesses and leaders within business:

Business leaders need to be able to think about their role in shaping climate outcomes; the future of work, jobs, and the workplace; the future of trust and truth; data privacy; and racial and social justice and equity. The opportunity you have in front of you is enormous, and I know your responsibility is too. But as the 2021 Edelman Trust Barometer[2] identified (and as we'll talk about in Chapter 20: A Brighter Future for Truth and Trust), corporate brands are some of the most trusted for leadership, so if this world is going to embrace the changes needed for a brighter future, we're going to need you to make them first. And don't look back.

Through the course of my work I have delivered keynote speeches at many events with executive audiences, and many of them come up to me after the talk to say my words and message about putting humans first resonates with them— but the struggle lies in putting the principles in place. They feel pressure from the board, from the rest of the C suite, from the market, from their investors, from their teams, and so on.

I know you want to make decisions that assure the success of your company, but you also want to be ethical, responsible with resources, and aligned with human outcomes. I hope this will give you a framework to take to your stakeholders to gain more buy-in. By all means, have them read this book too. Then more of you can be having the same conversation.

For makers of technology and tech-led experiences

I know you wonder about the ethical use of data—which, as you already know, is human data—and how to develop ethical approaches to human experiences in a future increasingly shaped by technology.

---

[2] https://www.edelman.com/trust/2021-trust-barometer

For many of you, being the voice of conscience in your company is a constant struggle. I hope this book will give you examples and vocabulary to use when arguing for the humans on the other side of the experiences you design and create.

For city leaders and leaders within cities:

Cities are a big part of the discussions on climate policy, data privacy, the future of work, housing, racial and social justice and equity, so I write and speak about these topics for city leaders often. You'll find here future-ready examples of initiatives happening now around the world, from cities large and small— hopeful examples that suggest integrative strategies from which you may be able to draw inspiration.

For leaders in nonprofits, museums, and other institutions:

Like everyone else, your programs are increasingly filled with discussions about climate, about justice, about technology; you have to wrestle with issues of trust and truth, and whose stories must be heard. Developing strategy for institutions right now is especially challenging, as you hold space for meaningful ideas and missions that still must confront the evolving realities of the external world. This book should offer hope for you, too, and examples that may help spark a light to shine on the important parts of humanity you represent.

And for everyone, everyday, wherever you are:

Leadership can come from anyone, anywhere. If a Swedish teenager with Asperger's syndrome can start by staging a weekly school strike to raise awareness of the climate crisis and within a few years become one of the best-known environmental activists in the world—as Greta Thunberg has—we must all be left to wonder what opportunities we may not be pursuing. How could we all make our commitments known?

Wherever you are, expect to find that everything is connected

Fundamentally, this book is about Strategic Optimism and how it can help us build the best futures for the most people. But in order to get there, we first have to talk about change, about priorities, and solving human problems at scale —as well as how everything is connected to everything else.

So along the way we'll cover the future of cities, climate change, innovation, robots and automation, artificial intelligence, the future of work, facial recognition and surveillance, ethics, the future of trust, algorithmic optimization, divided political discourse, and more broadly, the future of human experience. And how all of those things connect to one another.

We'll explore concepts across an array of topics that present challenges and opportunities to humanity heading into the future, from global warming to globalization, from automation to architecture. Along the way, some of the topics that have cropped up and demanded consideration have been:

• **Brain science and the latest research on thought itself**, to better understand how we humans process information and make decisions

• **Language and strategic framing**, to understand how to communicate the need for change with other people most effectively

• **Philosophy**, to delve into the ways we humans perceive the world and ponder our future, and what is meaningful to us

• **History**, to bear witness to what has already happened and what we should learn from it

• And of course **a broad coverage of science and technology topics**, to explore what options we have for improving the future at scale

Fortunately, these are all areas that perennially fascinate me, and I have done extensive reading on them over the years and in particular leading up to my work on this book. Not all of these topics are of equal importance to this book's central idea of using Strategic Optimism to achieve a brighter future, but for the ones that are, I've done the research to back it up. I've interviewed experts in many of these fields, read dozens of books and hundreds of studies on related topics, and literally hired a team of PhDs to help make sure we've examined the key concepts in depth.

My expertise and the focus of my work, however, has long been on the future of meaningful human experiences, and the impact of technology on the future of humanity. This book explores those two concepts across an array of topics, from the future of work to the future of truth and trust, from privacy to the economy.

So into this already dizzying mix of topics I have also added my direct knowledge and expertise, resulting in persistent themes and larger discussions: human experience, business strategy, technology as a whole, and the fundamental concept of meaning.

It's an honor to be able to present you with a synopsis of how all of these ideas, taken together, can best serve our future.

PART ONE:

Strategic Optimism

*The best results come about when we not only
visualize the best possible future
but also make a plan to commit ourselves to achieving it.*

Chapter 1:

A Bright Future Needs Optimism AND Strategy

Optimism won't save the world. At least, not on its own. Even the most hopeful outlook must be matched with clear-eyed recognition of the challenges ahead and a determination to meet them with a plan.

If we're feeling cute, we might even express this in a conceptual formula:

Optimism + Strategy = Bright Future

In other words, we need not *just* optimism, but **Strategic Optimism**: a clear acknowledgement of the state of the world, the problems we face, and the risks and harms before us—*as well as* a full accounting of the good we could do, the opportunities ahead, the solutions we could create, and the joy we could feel upon arriving in a better place. Whatever the best outcomes are, we need a consistent, steadfast, even stubborn insistence on achieving them.

Why optimism loves strategy and strategy loves optimism

Balance here is key. We may be tempted to spend too much time at the outset of any new development thinking strategically about what might go wrong and dreaming idly of what might go right. We certainly need to think and dream, but not at the expense of missing the part where we *apply strategic thinking* to that optimistic side to actually *achieve* the best outcomes.

In my advisory work, I promote optimism as an important part of future-ready strategy in the sense that without it, leaders can too easily adopt the status quo mentality or merely the small-scale, incremental changes that are trivial rather than visualize the better outcomes they could work toward and make bold moves toward them.

That means our focus and efforts are always more directed at containing the risks, at constraining the organic growth, at hampering whatever might come naturally. What comes naturally isn't always great, but if we spend more of that effort thinking in a disciplined way about what we want to go right, we could direct our resources in ways that cultivate the best outcomes anyway.

The arguments against optimism tend to focus on its lack of strategy and disconnection from reality. These viewpoints usually position some form of pessimism as the more pragmatic approach. As David Wallace-Wells writes in *The Uninhabitable Earth*, "When we dismiss the worst-case possibilities, it distorts our sense of likelier outcomes, which we then regard as extreme scenarios we needn't plan so conscientiously for." To which he adds: "The optimists have never, in the half century of climate anxiety we've already endured, been right.[3]"

It's a little odd, actually, that optimism is so often dismissed as naïveté because it's so often used as a proxy for positive outcomes in business-credible ways. *Chief Executive* magazine, for example, routinely measures "CEO optimism," and bull markets are often described as reflecting "investor optimism."

In fact, optimism makes a useful tool in an executive's toolbelt. As I said in a business article for American Express:

"People often seem to think optimism can only exist in the absence of any sensibility or pragmatism about the present or future, but in fact I think

---

[3] David Wallace-Wells, *The Uninhabitable Earth: Life After Warming* (New York: Crown, 2020), 9.

optimism works best as part of **a balanced set of tools**. I've jokingly called it 'hope as a service' (nerd alert), but even hope is only really useful when you train it the right outcomes—on what is most relevant to hope for.

"In other words, if you're running a big legacy company whose offering has been upended by newcomers in the space, it's useless to hope that things will return to the way they were when growth was easy for you. Change is inevitable, so hoping for reversal of change is fruitless. But optimism can allow you to envision a way forward for the company that draws from its heritage and origin story and also looks to the future with updated and adapted products, experiences, and technologies. Without the benefit of an optimistic outlook, it might be possible to recognize the severity of the company's situation but not be able to imagine a future where the company has found new relevance. If you can only recognize the severity, you'll manage conservatively: you'll cut costs, trim staff, etc. But you might not also invest in the as-yet-unproven new products and offerings the company could one day pivot to."[4]

But whatever the merits of optimism as an outlook, it's clear that to achieve outcomes that match our vision and hopeful determination, we must do the work of acknowledging the full and unvarnished reality that surrounds us and lies ahead of us. And once we can see what the best outcomes to work toward are, we must lay plans to achieve them.

Christiana Figueres and Tom Rivett-Carnac offer a lovely synopsis of optimism and how it works in their book, *The Future We Choose: Surviving the Climate Crisis*:

"To be optimistic, you must acknowledge the bad news that is all too readily available in scientific reports, your newsfeed, your Twitter account, and kitchen table conversations bemoaning our current state of affairs. More difficult, but necessary for any degree of change to take place, is to recognize the adversities and still be able to see that a different future is not only possible but is already tiptoeing into our daily lives. Without denying the bad news, you must make a point of focusing on all the good news regarding

---

[4] E. Napoletano, "Why Optimism Is an Essential Part of Effective Leadership," American Express, October 10, 2019, https://www.americanexpress.com/en-us/business/trends-and-insights/articles/why-optimism-is-an-essential-part-of-effective-leadership/.

climate change, such as the constantly dropping prices of renewables, an increasing number of countries taking on net-zero-emissions targets by 2050 or before, the multiple cities banning internal combustion vehicles, and the rising levels of capital shifting from the old to the new economy. None of this is happening yet at the necessary scale, but it is happening. Optimism is about being able to intentionally identify and prescribe the desired future so as to actively pull it closer."[5]

In short: Optimism unaccompanied by action will not get us to the brighter future.

We Start by Recognizing the Change Factors We Face

All these issues and elements we've listed a few times now—climate change, automation, etc.—demand a moniker of their own. We need a way to refer to them simply so they don't overwhelm us every time we list them.

For the sake of clarity, in the rest of this book we will refer to these collectively as the **Change Factors**.

As you think about the change you're facing in your own life, you may identify your own Change Factors. I encourage you to take the opportunity to spend some time thinking about what they are and write them down. You can even do it here; I've given you a line to start jotting down your answer. As you write them down, ask yourself a few questions about them:

- What are the forces compelling you to deal with change?

  _____

- What are the possible consequences of that change?

  _____

- What would the best possible outcomes be?

---

[5] Christiana Figueres and Tom Rivett-Carnac, *The Future We Choose: The Stubborn Optimist's Guide to the Climate Crisis* (New York: Knopf Doubleday, 2021), 44.

- Who could be harmed by the approach you're inclined to take?

- How could you avoid creating that harm?

- What are the risks of inaction?

When you have a sense of the fullness of these issues, you are ready to begin thinking about and planning for the best outcomes. We can't build a bright future without an understanding of our current reality.

"Optimism with a firm grasp on reality"

A few years ago when a team at Google first hired me to deliver a keynote at a team offsite, I asked the team leader on our prep call why she had chosen me. She said she liked that I was "optimistic about the role of tech in the future yet with a firm grasp on reality." I was charmed by that description, especially because I believe that's what the next phase of our collective tech future—and the work of addressing the future for humanity overall—needs to be:

optimistic but also cautionary,

with a heavy dose of realism and clarity.

Of course since my work primarily deals with emerging technology and its impact on humanity, I typically ground that perspective in a human-centric approach to tech and digital transformation, but I offer it to you as an expansive mindset that can apply to many aspects of future thinking and leadership.

I should acknowledge that I am often challenged about the need to detail and give voice to the dystopian possibilities of tech, and about the responsibility I have to represent and speak to the worst grievances. That charge is valid, and I do not—and none of us should—shy away from calling out the worst offenders and injustices. In fact, I make the dangers within the data and big tech space abundantly clear in my talks and writing. But my emphasis more often than not is on the opportunity for us to do better, to build meaningful futures. That's because my sense is that when people only hear about how awful a situation is, they're more likely to think it's hopeless to work toward better outcomes. (That feels like where we've been stuck for quite some years now regarding the climate crisis, for example.) Better outcomes are always possible, though, and especially given the power of technology, we have an existentially moral responsibility to work toward them.

In other words, I'm not saying we don't have a problem; I'm saying I *know* we have a problem, and I believe we can and must address it and do better.

"Pull no punches"

That same Google exec also asked me to "pull no punches." The audience wanted a realistic view of what their decisions were doing in the world, and I applaud them for welcoming that. Google is far from a perfect company with perfect leadership making perfect decisions, but they made a savvy call in asking an external speaker to give it to them straight. That's the only path to progress, after all; it takes guts to look the reality in the face and still be committed to doing the work necessary to put things on the right track.

There is perhaps no more optimistic mindset than the one of alignment: the idea that you can find symbiosis between you and another person or organization. You do this by looking for synergy in your gaps and their gaps, or your gaps and their opportunities. It can work either way.

An optimistic view of the future also implies that we have a responsibility to work toward better outcomes. Because if we can see them, aren't we ethically obligated to pursue them? That commitment may be daunting to some people— if only because it's easier to remain cynical about what's possible than to obligate yourself to a path requiring changes in mindset and behavior.

For Strategic Optimism to work for us, it *must* be about commitment. Hope without action is nothing more than daydreaming. Hope *with* action is the only way we make progress.

Besides, I find that people don't respond well to doomsaying. It doesn't motivate them the way hope does.

When you accept optimism as a default, you can assess your circumstances quite candidly and work toward the best outcome. Pessimism, after all, is no more than acceptance of the worst. Optimism means you have to *work for* the best.

So we must remain optimistic but with an eye on the risks you face so you don't let them sneak up on you.

It's hard to grasp how much of the challenge of distraction by politics is due to the amplification of social media, and how much is politics just being a dumpster fire. Whichever it is, it is undeniably hard to concentrate, let alone feel optimistic about the state of the world.

But we can take guidance from what might seem an unlikely source: Noam Chomsky. In his speech "Why I Choose Optimism over Despair," Chomsky says:

> "The task for social policy is to design the ways we live and the institutional and cultural structure of our lives so as to favor the benign and to suppress the harsh and destructive aspects of our fundamental nature."[6]

Perhaps we can read this as not just the task for social policy, per se, but as the role of our social contract with each other and ourselves. Favor the benign; suppress the harsh and destructive. Across every area of our work and our lives. Again and again, as much as we need to in order to make a brighter future.

We have the tools to build the future we envision

This future doesn't exist, though; we have to build it. But that's okay because we have the tools.

---

[6] Noam Chomsky and C. J. Polychroniou "Optimism over Despair: On Capitalism, Empire, and Social Change, Part III. Why I Choose Optimism over Despair" > Location 2988

What is Strategic Optimism, exactly?

Let's start with what Strategic Optimism is *not*:

Strategic Optimism is not "the power of positive thinking."

Positive thinking is appealing for many and arguably important as guidance for aligning resources and focusing efforts. But I find its most devout adherents often take its application too far and apply it too literally.

It can quickly turn into an ugly case of victim blaming—as in, if you don't have everything, you must not be thinking positively enough. For example: Got cancer? Why don't you just think your way out of it?

That's not at all the mindset we're looking for here. Where the positivity principles do make sense is in aligning with our experience. The key is that framing our goals in terms of positive outcomes as opposed to negative ones—e.g., "I want to be wealthy" instead of "I don't want to be broke"—generally lends itself to a stronger overall ability to focus and rally resources. It makes a very simple kind of sense: There is momentum in the positive, whereas the negative is all about stopping, and there's no forward motion in that. Life is all about forward motion, so it's practical to use a mental model that aligns with our experience and feels like it accompanies us as we move through time and space.

It's not a matter of "law of attraction" or "power of positive thinking," but rather of accepting that perceived limitations change our actions. If we let our beliefs limit us, we are guaranteed not to try.

Strategic Optimism is not about ignoring the limitations, risks, or harms that do exist; in fact, it's about *acknowledging* the full reality of the current situation and the full range of possible outcomes, mitigating the worst outcomes, and working diligently toward achieving the best.

So what *is* Strategic Optimism, then?

The best results come about when we not only visualize the best possible future but also make a plan to commit ourselves to achieving it. This by necessity entails some variation of making goals, creating timelines, and sticking to them. In other words, developing some kind of strategy to achieve what you are hoping for.

Laying out a plan also means acknowledging the risks and harms that could occur and developing more plans to mitigate those, but also spending time on *the ways the plan could go right* and investing effort in ensuring those positive results come to fruition.

When we lay out our plans for the future, we know that we need to acknowledge the risks, but we often forget to spend as much time thinking about the opportunities. This can actually cost us: We might underestimate how successful a new product could be, for instance, and fail to have a way to meet demand; we might negotiate well below the value of our contributions in a job or a project; we might be so preoccupied with worst-case scenarios that when our moment to shine takes us by surprise, we're fully unprepared for it.

Taking the time to work through the process means visualizing the boldest, most optimistic outcomes that will help us achieve the best futures. Visualization might sound like so much self-help and junk science, but in fact it's been proven empirically in study after study. The science of human thought has come to appreciate, for example, the link between ideas in the abstract and our embodied understanding of them—that when we imagine actions and objects, we engage the actual parts of our brains that would engage with them if we performed them or encountered them in reality. Athletes who train using positive visualization techniques perform better in competition, while athletes who visualize negative outcomes perform worse than if they had done no training at all[7]. American swimmer Katie Ledecky has often talked about how she not only visualizes her goals but even how her stroke should feel throughout her races[8]—and that approach has led her to Olympic gold medals and being named world champion at least 15 times. Why would the rest of us not benefit from similar mental exercises?

---

[7] from Louder Than Words: The New Science of How the Mind Makes Meaning by Benjamin K. Bergen

[8] Swim Swam, "Ledecky explains pre race visualization rituals (Video)" August 6, 2016. https://swimswam.com/ledecky-explains-pre-race-visualization-rituals-video/

What we imagine for ourselves has powerful influence in shaping the way we think, the way we behave, the language we choose, the opportunities we seek out. If we believe no improvement is possible, we will seek no improvement. And because this book is written for humans, this link matters.

What do you see when you imagine the future?

Is it a dark and mysterious scene straight out of an apocalyptic sci-fi thriller, full of arid landscapes, warring factions, and laser gun battles?

I'll wager that you don't envision an eden with lush green spaces, peaceful people, and technology that empowers life. Most would agree that this vision of the future sounds good. Most would also suspect that such a future is not achievable. Part of the reason why people don't think it's achievable is because we've been trained to think about the future in a limited way.

Perhaps you have heard this before, but there's an interesting—albeit depressing—analogy about elephants. When they are young and small, trainers may tie their legs to wooden stumps with ropes or chain that the young calves are not yet strong enough to break. They learn that they cannot escape this tether. As they grow, they reach a size and strength where they could easily rip an entire tree from the ground, but because all the elephants' lives they understood that they were limited, a trainer only needs a thin rope on a tiny tree to restrain them. It's the darker subtext behind the adage "an elephant never forgets."

We too have enormous potential we have been conditioned—or have conditioned ourselves—not to acknowledge, and limitations we suppose exist but which at any moment, with a fraction of our collective strength, we could overpower. With Strategic Optimism, even as we refuse to be in denial, we still believe some kind of progress is possible. Strategic Optimism means envisioning the best outcomes, and knowing that by acknowledging the inherent possibility of these outcomes, that we are ethically obligated to pursue them.

Optimism may set the stage for better outcomes and may well even be contagious. Can we do a better job of solving the problems that humanity faces if we *behave as though*—not *wondering if*—we can?

Objectivity, compassion, and determination are three of the characteristics of Strategic Optimism. We need the clarity and rationalism of objectivity to see things as they are, the empathy and awareness that come with compassion to

23

see how decisions affect others, and the stubbornness of determination to commit to making things better.

Why is this not pragmatism or realism? Because many times these mindsets fool us into thinking we must work toward a middle ground. Strategic Optimism obligates us to work toward the best outcomes we can envision. So even if the intermediate steps and results are incremental, the mindset is not *incrementalist*. It may *look* like incrementalism when circumstances constrain its effect, but this kind of optimism is by its nature radically progressive as it aligns itself to the best outcomes as an ethical guide.

This deliberate approach to optimism is intentionally radical and bound to equity. In fact, it is less about the feel-good optimistic mindset, per se, and more about the strategy that follows from the optimism: the commitment to change for the better, and to the work we know we must do to achieve the best possible futures for the most people.

This way of thinking rests on solidly democratic principles. People are going to disagree about priorities, after all, and it is not for one class of people to decide upon them for the others. This implies an emphasis on stakeholder involvement. I'm not advocating for a techno-utopia, or Silicon Valley as savior, or blind trust that the market can fix problems (problems the market, in many cases, helped to create).

This approach asks everyone to assume their responsibilities and hold other entities accountable.

Chapter 2:

The Strategic Optimism Model: BRIGHTER

BEFORE WE DIG INTO THE Strategic Optimism Model and the Human Superpowers that drive it, let's consider a few foundational goals that aren't part of the framework exactly but are still important to remember as we begin visualizing best possible outcomes.

Start from inclusivity. Start from the most inclusive view of humanity, of the planet.

Emphasize alignment. It's a plus when a brand or entity stands for some kind of social movement out of nowhere, but it's much more memorable—and therefore much more meaningful—when the stance aligns with the organization in some way, whether because of purpose, community involvement, or some other relevant factor.

Aim to be on the right side of history. Years in the future, when people look back on the defining moments of our present era, make sure your leadership counted for something.

So how can we use our Human Superpowers to solve problems large and small? With Strategic Optimism, which looks like this[9]:

Introducing the Strategic Optimism Model: BRIGHTER

1. **Be bold and honest** about the fullness of the situation, even if it initially looks bleak

2. **Recognize** what matters (hint: this is *meaning*!)

3. **Identify** what is going to matter (hint: this is where *innovation* comes in!)

4. **Go all in on hope** as a tool of focus and refocus

5. **Habituate** to change (meaning: get used to it!)

6. **Tune in with empathy** to anticipate what needs to change

7. **Envision bold** ways forward

8. **Resolve to work** toward the best futures for the most people

Most of these are innate skills we have as humans; we just don't always remember to use them. That's why I like to think of them as being complemented by our Human Superpowers, which we'll explore more fully in a moment. But in the next few pages, we'll unpack each step of the Strategic Optimism Model and delve into what makes the steps work separately and what makes the whole thing work so well together.

---

[9] Dear reader, I've never been a fan of using acronyms to spell out conceptual models, but I'm committed to doing everything I can to make this work.

Be bold and honest in assessing the problems we face

B	Be bold and honest about the situation, even if it initially looks bleak
R	Recognize *what matters* (hint: this is *meaning*!)
I	Identify *what is going to matter* (hint: this is where *innovation* comes in!)
G	Go all in on hope as a tool of focus and refocus
H	Habituate to change (meaning: get used to it!)
T	Tune in with empathy to anticipate what needs to change
E	Envision bold ways forward
R	Resolve to work toward the best futures for the most people

Imagine you're on a road trip with your friend in their car when the engine sputters and breaks down. You may *want* to help, you may *try* to help, and you may even have the skills to help, but until you look under the hood and assess what's actually wrong, you're not going to *be* much help.

When it comes to the Change Factors facing humanity at a global scale, we can't develop much of a strategy, optimistic or otherwise, without facing the true scope of the challenges. And that means we must not only *acknowledge* the fullness of the problems we must solve in a bold and blunt way, but also we must sit with the implications and impacts of them and allow their magnitude to sink in. Only with that full understanding will we be most prepared to address the challenges with the seriousness and commitment they deserve.

To do that we need to listen to those who are expert in plumbing the depths and breadths of the problems: the scholars, scientists, educators, activists, and others who are committed to studying and working with the issues that shape our lives.

We also need to listen to the people who are part of the communities most fundamentally affected by the problems we are examining. We'd be foolish to propose accessibility solutions, for example, without talking with people who are disabled and who spend their lives navigating accessibility shortcomings. When we think about the climate crisis, we must account for and understand the needs of people who are already suffering the "weirding" conditions of climate, from wildfires to floods, and those whose homes are likely to be displaced by the next stages, as arctic ice thaws and sea levels rise, and as climate refugees inevitably become a constant fixture of our global discourse.

Most of all we need to listen to the intersection of these two groups: the experts who are part of the communities affected by the problem. Our insights must be guided by them, not merely influenced by them.

As author and CEO coach Marshall Goldsmith writes, "The most famous poem in history is probably the Bhagavad Gita. And the Gita has very good advice for this. Basically, you have a person who's got two decisions to make. One is bad, and the other is worse. The message is: First, you accept what is. You don't hide from what it is. Then, you don't get fixated on the outcome. You can't control the outcome. You have a goal, but if your ego gets attached to the goal, you're in trouble. Then, you focus on what are you doing? What's my strategy? What am I doing now? Am I doing the right thing? Am I doing my best?"[10]

Some of you are thinking: "Wait, this doesn't sound like optimism." If it doesn't, in my view, you've been thinking about optimism in a way that doesn't work. Cherry-picking the most favorable "facts" and the best results isn't optimism; it's denial. And denial isn't going to lead us to the best outcomes; only objectivity, compassion, and determination will do that.

---

[10] Dan Bigman,
"'Be Human': Marshall Goldsmith's Best Leadership Advice Right Now," *Chief Executive*, September 11, 2020, https://chiefexecutive.net/be-human-marshall-goldsmiths-best-leadership-advice-right-now/.

Recognize what matters: Meaning as the core Human Superpower

B	Be bold and honest about the situation, even if it initially looks bleak
R	Recognize *what matters* (hint: this is *meaning*!)
I	Identify *what is going to matter* (hint: this is where *innovation* comes in!)
G	Go all in on hope as a tool of focus and refocus
H	Habituate to change (meaning: get used to it!)
T	Tune in with empathy to anticipate what needs to change
E	Envision bold ways forward
R	Resolve to work toward the best futures for the most people

Humor me for a second. I'm going to ask you to play a little game with me, if you will. Think of a word—just one word—that for you sort of epitomizes what the human experience is all about. When you think about what defines the human condition, or what really characterizes human existence? What, for you, is that one word that really distills what it means to be human?

When I ask this question to most audiences, there are usually a few common answers, and they fall into a few groupings of ideas.

Some people say creativity, problem solving, or innovation.

Even more people give answers like compassion, emotions, empathy, or love.

And while those are all indeed compelling traits of human beings, I tend to think there's one missing—and that one answer is the most fundamental and most unique aspect of being human:

Humans crave *meaning*.

We seek meaning, and we attempt to make meaning from everything. Our greatest tendency is our greatest strength—how we want to see patterns and purpose in everything. Meaning is, in a sense, our core Human Superpower. As far as we know, we are the only species who comprehends meaning; who thinks about what things mean; who is self-aware enough to ponder our own existence. We don't yet know of animals with this capacity or trait, and so far, machines don't do that either. So humans, as far as we know, are the only animals or species or whatever who considers meaning.

When I'm talking about meaning, I'm talking about many meanings of meaning. I'm a linguist by education, so I always joke that I get semantics for free. But all these other kinds of meaning are things I've collected over the years. I've done thirty years of study on what meaning really is; I've been fascinated with meaning most of my life, and for almost as long, I've been collecting theories of meaning and how meaning is applied in our lives and what we mean when we talk about meaning. And so, let's take one of these meanings of meaning and drill into it: *significance*.

What's fun about the word *significance* is that you can break it into related words such as *signify* and *significant*. And when you're talking about what something *signifies*, you're talking about what it conveys, represents, or tries to communicate. And then *significant* is all about what's important and what matters. So you've got these these embedded packages of dimension that happen even within and around these related words.

When you zoom back out, you can think about how meaning is present in all of those definitions—meaning that meaning is always about what matters. When we think about meaning, whether we think about it in a more semantic, language-centric way or a more cosmic, existential way, what we are always examining is **what matters**.

We're always looking for significance. We're always trying to understand what matters. As we learn to harness this trait, this dimension of meaning and meaningfulness, it becomes **our core Human Superpower**. It helps us understand what matters.

There's this other meaning of meaning, which is *purpose*. Many books and thought leaders talk about purpose because it is such a fundamental Human Superpower. Purpose is what happens when meaning finds action. It's about *putting intention around what matters*.

And then there's relevance. Relevance is a *shared understanding of what matters*.

Meaningful experiences

At one level or another, both this book and my work overall are about human experiences. In particular, they ask this question: what kind of strategy and thinking can help us create the experiences best suited for changes at scale in the future? My proposed answer to that question will probably not surprise you at this point: one of the recurring themes of my research and analysis within the field of human experience strategy is how to create the most *meaningful* experiences.

It turns out that the way humans make meaning depends heavily on our experiences. So meaning and experiences are already linked in one direction, and we have the opportunity to bring them full circle. Put another way: Our experiences are fundamental to the way we humans understand meaning, and meaning is fundamental to how we experience the world.

This idea of meaning as central to the context of human experiences is a clue to help us design intentional experiences with a focus on *what matters*: what matters in the alignment of the relationship between a company, say, and the person outside the company who is perhaps its product's user. Or a brand and the person who is its consumer, or a city and the person who is its resident or visitor.

Note that in every one of those examples, the emphasis is on the person, not the role that the person happens to be fulfilling in any given transaction or encounter. Customer experience, for example, as a discipline focuses on the strategies and tactics needed to deliver value in the buying transaction and lifecycle, but it doesn't fulfill the same insights as human experience strategy. They're both important—they just happen at a different level. It's like zooming out to the macro human perspective or zooming in to the more specific role, like user experience, patient experience, guest, student, visitor, etc.

This focus on what matters at every level plugs us in to the current of meaning, which in turn helps us connect to what the human in question is actually experiencing, or taking away from the interaction—and completing that logical circuit helps us deliver more meaningful, memorable human experiences overall.

It also helps us to understand that the great business topic of *purpose* is fundamentally a discussion about meaningful human experience, and about what matters. While plenty of business books talk about purpose, the insight that lights it up to its full potential is the realization that **purpose is the shape that meaning takes in business**.

So using purpose as a key input to strategy means assessing, on a one-time and perhaps a periodic basis, what the driving principle of the individual or the organization is: what the company, for example, exists to do and is trying to do at scale.

Purpose has value at the individual level, too: assessing our own purpose can help us recognize what drives us, what makes us feel accomplished, what connects us with the people around us, and how to be mindful of those values and priorities as we engage with technology such as social media so that the tech we use can actually enhance our lives.

When an organization assesses its purpose and principles, the exercise gives greater clarity to everything that flows from that articulation: values, priorities, brand considerations, experience design, and so on, all the way out to data modeling and tech deployment.

A counterargument to this emphasis on meaning in future-looking experience strategy and design might claim that since meaning is about as high as you can get on Maslow's hierarchy of needs, we should focus primarily on rectifying matters that are more basic and fundamental. I do not argue with prioritizing basic needs. I support the experts who work in fields more directly related to housing and food justice. What I have found, though, through my own expertise in experience strategy, is that the characteristics of human meaning can be used to dimensionalize any of that work. In my New York neighborhood of Hell's Kitchen, we have a "Free Store"[11] where people can leave household items they don't need and others may take what they like. This idea matters because it is helpful for neighbors who might find useful odds and

---

[11] https://www.instagram.com/hkfreestore/

ends they wouldn't otherwise have money to buy, and it also creates a small circular economy that may be keeping products out of landfills. Mutual aid programs and pay-what-you-can models are further approaches to providing for people's basic needs that can strengthen communities as well as an individual's sense of agency. Meaning may not be a physiological need, per se, but it is certainly a psychological need, and while we are addressing people's needs for food and shelter, for example, it's important we do so with an understanding of dignity and the sense of self. These are key to human thriving, no matter what problem we are trying to solve, and they are part of the meaningful experience of being alive as a human being.

Watch out for absurdity

Even amid the meaningful events of human life, we encounter absurd moments. Absurdity is not exactly the inverse of meaning, but it exists in a kind of tension with meaning. That tension can be enlightening, such as in surrealist art: "Ceci n'est pas une pipe." But for the purposes of experience design, the general principle is: where meaning is well defined, absurdity is scarce, and where there is absurdity, meaning struggles to exist.

It's the absurd human experiences created by technology that threaten to overtake our world. Absurd in the sense that we don't know whether to say please and thank you to our voice assistants. It's absurd every time we have to check an "I'm not a robot" box to "confirm" our humanity to a machine. It's absurd being in an Amazon Go grocery store and not being able to take products off of the shelves for other shoppers who need our help at risk of being charged for their products. It's a "this is not a pipe" version of reality without the enlightenment. Scale raises the stakes on the design of interactions and shines a spotlight on anywhere we forgot to build in a sense of meaning and what matters. That's an easy problem to have because "what matters" may seem straightforward at first but may change dramatically with scale. Experience at scale changes culture. Because experience at scale *is* culture.

We don't want to let absurd interactions and experiences scale into an absurd culture. In the near term, absurdity is a far greater risk than full-blown dystopia. This is part of the language we're missing to discuss the future. We talk about the freedom of automation replacing meaningless and trivial tasks, but as more and more of our human experiences are automated, if we want to avoid scaling absurdity, we will want these experiences to be infused with a human sense of meaning.

Identify what is going to matter: Innovation through a human-centric lens

B	Be bold and honest about the situation, even if it initially looks bleak
R	Recognize *what matters* (hint: this is *meaning*!)
I	Identify *what is going to matter* (hint: this is where *innovation* comes in!)
G	Go all in on hope as a tool of focus and refocus
H	Habituate to change (meaning: get used to it!)
T	Tune in with empathy to anticipate what needs to change
E	Envision bold ways forward
R	Resolve to work toward the best futures for the most people

If you take the idea that meaning, one of our most defining human traits and our core Human Superpower, is about what matters and then apply it forward to thinking about the future, to what innovations will need to happen in order to address what will matter, you will have inherently taken a human-centric approach to innovation.

The most human-centric way to think about innovation is to ask, "What is going to matter?"

Meaning is about what matters. Innovation is about what is going to matter.

This is why it's important to keep one eye on now and one eye on the future, as we'll talk about in Envision bold ways forward. These two ways of looking at the world may seem contradictory, but in practice their inherent contrasts can illuminate a lot about each other. With that clarity, we can draw a through-line from what matters—or: what is meaningful—in this present moment to what is going to matter—or: what our innovation should be—in the brighter future we want to create.

How do we determine what is going to matter?

The challenging thing about making the best decisions for the future is that we experience the world in the here and now through our senses, and our senses make meaning. What we can see, hear, taste, smell, and touch all bear heavier on our decision-making than what we think, imagine, or feel, even if we intend to do the right thing. Our brains fire on embodied experiences, and our cognitive faculties are wired to come alive through our senses. So delayed gratification is really hard.

Which is where this model of innovation comes in handy: The more we can ground our approach to the future in terms of human meaning, the better the chance that it will resonate with us and remain a vivid priority. Innovation built on meaning requires an emphasis on meaningful human experiences.

Meaningful human experiences are

- Relevant
- Dimensional
- Aligned
- Intentional
- Context-aware

Inside businesses, when innovation programs are being evaluated, it can be tough to make the case for far-reaching projects that aren't grounded in benefits we can feel and taste now. But the shape meaning takes in business is purpose, and we can look for alignment with the company's purpose to find opportunities to make the priorities stick.

Look for opportunities to create alignment

You will no doubt have noticed that the title of this book is a not-very-subtle reference to an '80s pop song that calls for shades. It's a playful tie-in for me personally, as I have for decades rarely been seen without sunglasses on top of my head. My favorite pairs come from Parafina, a sunglasses brand whose products are made from recycled materials like tires and HDPE and PET plastic. They're also a B-Corp that donates 5 percent of their income to giving kids access to primary school supplies in Paraguay.

Every business has an opportunity to connect the core of their work with meaningful extensions into areas that support humankind, to align their innovation with human outcomes and the health of the planet as a whole, and to help solve human problems at scale.

The investments you make in innovative projects don't always pay returns right away, but they will let you learn directionally. The point is to set a course that you can then align your perspective through, from what is urgent and important today to what you believe may be important in the future. The straight line you visualize that runs from now through the important stuff of the future gives you clarity about what your priorities may need to be in the days, weeks, and years ahead.

But what if you succeed?

With emerging technologies, our actions and decisions will have outsized consequences as every small detail has the capacity to reach massive scale. That means something that seems trivial when only a few people use it will change culture by the time millions of people are using it every day. Deploying optimism in this context would encourage us to use best-case scenario planning, which allows teams to avoid unintended consequences. In other words, one question I encourage product teams to ask themselves is: "What will it look like if this project or product *succeeds beyond your wildest imaginings*?" Once we have that vision, it is easier to see the ways in which we may unintentionally be scaling biases, cultural weirdnesses, and other consequences.

Go all in on hope as a tool of focus and re-focus

B	Be bold and honest about the situation, even if it initially looks bleak
R	Recognize *what matters* (hint: this is *meaning*!)
I	Identify *what is going to matter* (hint: this is where *innovation* comes in!)
G	Go all in on hope as a tool of focus and refocus
H	Habituate to change (meaning: get used to it!)
T	Tune in with empathy to anticipate what needs to change
E	Envision bold ways forward
R	Resolve to work toward the best futures for the most people

Whenever we were talking about strategy, an old boss of mine would often quip, "False hope feels like real hope"; and he meant that even illusory signals of positivity can be encouraging. I liked this boss and I knew what he meant when he used the phrase, but I always found the underlying premise troubling.

Hope is a tool too important to waste on falsehood. It's a direction we set for the work we are passionate enough to do. To me, the only hope worth clinging to is one that feels aligned with our understanding of reality. We use hope to light the way ahead of ourselves toward the outcome we want, and the very act of determining that outcome tells us something about ourselves and about our surroundings. Hope points to opportunities fear would have us overlook. In that sense, it is innovation's greatest ally. When you can see your circumstances for what they are and feel a pull toward a particular outcome, that's hope. Hope is telling you what you want to have happen. The marvelous thing about hope, though, is that we can decide what to hope for. What you hope for can change from one moment to the next as the circumstances of reality change, but no matter what, your hope always tells you where to direct your energy and efforts.

But you can't figure out what it is you truly want if you don't allow yourself to have genuine hope. Hope is what you use to tell yourself the honest truth.

"The kind of hope I often think about...I understand above all as a state of mind, not a state of the world. Either we have hope within us, or we don't...Hope is not prognostication. It is an orientation of the spirit, an orientation of the heart."

— **Václav Havel**, 1936-2011: Czech playwright turned dissident turned president[12]

Optimism as we are using it here, after all, doesn't mean not recognizing the negative possibilities, the dangers, the harms, or the people who don't believe that good results can happen; it means that amidst everything you see the best possible outcome and let that be the focus of your committed work.

If you come to a ledge with a chasm between you and the next ledge, you have to decide what the likely scenarios are if you jump. Out of the likely scenarios, you may recognize that you're untrained in distance jumping and unlikely to cross the gap safely. Would you hope for the best and jump anyway? It probably depends on the other factors involved: Is a wild animal chasing you? Do you have time to scope out alternative routes?

If we allow optimism to feel like "blind hope" (if you'll pardon my invoking an ableist metaphor) or false hope, we're missing out on the power of hope as a tool of focus and refocus. It does no good to hope for things that can't happen. Of course, hope has to operate in the context of reality or it can lead to disaster. It's important to see clearly what the real harms are, what dangers lurk, what problems you can create for yourself or for others as you proceed down your path with your plans.

Hope versus the Change Factors

All is not lost.

---

[12] as quoted in *Disturbing the Peace: A conversation with Karel Hvížďala*, (Knopf, 1990), p. 181. Originally published 1986. Translated from the Czech by Paul Wilson.

In fact, we have more reason than ever to act with urgency about the pressing changes shaping humanity and the world, but we also have more resources than ever to deal with them.

When in doubt I'll always defer to the wise words of Rebecca Solnit: "Hope is an ax you break down doors with in an emergency...hope should shove you out the door, because it will take everything you have to steer the future away from endless war, from the annihilation of the earth's treasures and the grinding down of the poor and marginal...To hope is to give yourself to the future, and that commitment to the future makes the present inhabitable."[13]

There's another kind of cliché phrase that annoys me: "Hope is not a strategy." This implication is: "Don't bother with hope because it's not a plan." It bugs me every time I hear it, because obviously no, hope is not the same thing as a strategy. As both a self-identified hopeful person and a strategist, I can say that with confidence. But it seems like another implication of "hope is not a strategy" is that *pessimism is* somehow more strategic.

But believe me: Pessimism is not a strategy either. It doesn't do you any good to think *only* about what could go wrong. It does do *some* good to think about what could go wrong, but it does you just as much good to think about what could go right. And yet we tend to spend a lot of time on what could go wrong and less time on what could go right.

And a lot of times what could go wrong happens as a result of not having thought about what could go right. So we need to spend our time in the hope and optimism space. Those are Human Superpowers we really need to go deep on.

"Our new intentional direction must move us beyond defeatism to optimism, beyond extraction toward regeneration, beyond linear toward circular economies, beyond individual benefit toward the common good, beyond short-term thinking toward long-term thinking and acting. By cultivating the three mindsets, we give clearer, stronger direction to our lives and to our world, setting the

---

[13] Rebecca Solnit, *Hope in the Dark: Untold Histories, Wild Possibilities* (Chicago: Haymarket Books, 2016), 4.

necessary foundation for us to collectively co-create the world we want."

—Christiana Figueres and Tom Rivett-Carnac, *The Future We Choose: Surviving the Climate Crisis*[14]

Hope is courageous. As animals by nature, we are programmed to look for danger, to be attuned to the risks around us. Those are good survival instincts, but by themselves they are insufficient to the evolved species we have become: the collective creators of civilizations, of cultures, of human flourishing and promise. We have everything we need to create better and better worlds for ourselves, for the generations to come, and for all the living things on this planet. But to do so requires our first setting our mind to the possibility.

---

[14] Figueres and Rivett-Carnac, *The Future We Choose*, 40.

Habituate to change (meaning: get used to it!)

B	**Be bold and honest** about the situation, even if it initially looks bleak
R	**Recognize** *what matters* (hint: this is *meaning*!)
I	**Identify** *what is going to matter* (hint: this is where *innovation* comes in!)
G	**Go all in on hope** as a tool of focus and refocus
H	**Habituate to change** (meaning: get used to it!)
T	**Tune in with empathy** to anticipate what needs to change
E	**Envision bold ways forward**
R	**Resolve** to work toward the best futures for the most people

When we deal with exponential change, or with any kind of big change at all, we are often left trying to navigate situations that are—to use a word that has seen a lot of use since the beginning of 2020—*unprecedented*. In fact so many people wrote so much about how the COVID-19 pandemic was unprecedented that the word *unprecedented* began to enjoy unprecedented popularity within Google search trends.

So I found that I was asked to talk with people about the tools that I know for dealing with how to think about the future, as someone who's been working for decades now around technology, futurism, and digital transformation.

For years I had felt that the central, driving question of my work was: "How can humanity prepare for an increasingly tech- and data-driven future?" But the more time I spent talking with people about how they were navigating the changes of the COVID-19 pandemic, the more it revealed an underlying question, related but broader: "Because so many things affect so many other things, how can humanity prepare for a future that's filled with exponential change?" The conversation and the questions have changed because during this time, we've recognized more and more that everything is connected.

So by asking, "How can humanity prepare for a future of exponential change?" I feel like what we're really asking is:

"How can humanity prepare for anything?"

And:

"How can we deal with the change that comes from anything?"

Change, as they say, is a constant. We will be dealing with it all our lives, in all areas of our lives. So we might as well **habituate to change**—or, in other words, get used to it.

How do we do that?

By working with clients and audiences through the early part of the pandemic, I realized that the tools I use to think about the future—the same tools I have used to navigate unprecedented changes at other times in my career and in my personal life—are intrinsically human tools. Those human tools are traits like hope, empathy, adaptability, meaning, imagination, and so on. They're the very tools I am exploring in this book in the context of our collective futures, because I think what we're really coming to understand is that the question boils down to: How can we, as humans, be prepared for, be habituated to, and learn to thrive in *any* kind of change?

I find that everything we need to cope with change is already in us, in the form of what I now like to call our Human Superpowers. Our humanity grants us the superpowers that help us deal with change.

This approach works at every level, from global to personal and back again

This hopeful, adaptive, meaning-filled approach to dealing with massive change is very personal for me, and very grounded in reality and lived experience. Like many of us, I have experienced my share of life changes that were challenging for me. And like some of us, I have also experienced the kind of profoundly life-altering change that challenged me to see any way in which the future could possibly still be bright: In 2012, my late husband died suddenly by suicide. It threw my entire world into disarray and changed everything I thought I knew about the future. One moment my life was normal, a regular

Monday morning, and the next moment, I was in an entirely different life. Like, *seismically* different. It felt surreal, as though I was trapped in a scene from a bizarre and disturbing horror movie.[15]

But from that tragic and traumatic experience, amid the reflection and processing I did after, I realized that some of what I was equipped with to handle my situation came from years of working with change in other contexts. I already intuitively understood how to deal with substantive change. What I found was that the kind of change I had helped companies manage in a professional context, the kind of change I had helped analyze and develop strategies for—these were not so different, at least operationally, from profound personal change. In taking stock of what helped me get through the days after my husband died, the next few breaths I forced myself to take after the realization, the minutes and hours that followed, and the days that eventually became weeks and the months that ultimately became years, a lot of what turned out to be most useful and most helpful to me in navigating that enormous change in my life was fundamentally the same kinds of things I had been advising clients to do around transformations—digital and otherwise—in their workspaces.

If that sounds like a stretch, consider how change of any kind is deeply personal. Even when it happens in your workplace, it affects you personally and you often react to it viscerally. Many of the reasons why digital transformations, strategic transformations, and cultural transformations sputter, stall, or fail entirely is because they meet with human resistance to change on a personal level.

Transformations are probably happening in your world right now. Many of the same ideas apply, and there's a great deal of richness to be found in what we already know as humans about how to navigate change.

Transformation: digital, cultural, or personal

When something changes from one form into another, it transforms—which is why this is such a critical piece of the Strategic Optimism Model. Part of the

---

[15] Apologies if this is triggering for some to read. If you are struggling at all, please talk to someone. Here is the suicide hotline in the US: 1-800-273-8255.
And you can find one in other countries in this list:
https://en.wikipedia.org/wiki/List_of_suicide_crisis_lines.

work of any organization is transforming culture into brand, and both culture and brand into experiences.

The hot topic of the past decade or so has been *digital* transformation. Just about every organization in the world is on a journey to develop stronger digital tools, greater clarity from analytics, and overall greater agility with data. Digital transformation is transforming business models and practices to align with data-centered commerce and optimization. Part of that effort is workplace transformation—readying the organization, infrastructure, etc., to deal with remote workers and distributed teams, contract and freelance employees, robots of all kinds, virtual workflows, and so on. Another part of the effort is job transformation—recognizing the evolution of roles and job scopes, and making elegant transitions from person to person, team to team, resource to resource. (That last point is a significant portion of the discussion in the section on Meaningful Work and Jobs.)

The point that always strikes me about the overall idea of digital transformation, though, is that data, as I have long said, is people. In other words, most of the data in business is fundamentally *about* people, in that it is captured through people's interactions and describes their activities: what they want to buy, how they respond to offers, where they go to fulfill their needs, who their friends and influencers are, and so on.

That's why I developed the model of Human-Centric Digital Transformation, as I wrote about in *Tech Humanist*. Human-Centric Digital Transformation is iterative, informed by data, and by definition, centered on human experiences.

Businesses are the drivers of most human experiences. Note that I don't make the argument that business is inherently more worthy, more virtuous, more capable, or has any more justification to create human experiences than any other type of entity—only that it is the case. And as such, it is to humanity's benefit for business to be equipped with tools to create the best possible human experiences.

We talk about digital transformation because technology is making ever faster cycles of change in all facets of our lives, and the workplace is one facet we think we can control. Or perhaps it's the one over which we think we should *exert* the most control.

As I wrote in the Tech Humanist Manifesto[16]:

> "We talk about 'digital transformation' in business. But let's be honest: most corporate environments are anything but transformative. So we need to begin to re-imagine and yes, transform business operations and culture around new models of infrastructure, new understandings of the social contract between employer and employee, and fundamentally new ideas of value. Because our world is increasingly integrated: online and offline, at work and at play, and we have to be wholly integrated selves, too."

After all, our lives are too separated and compartmentalized. I've written before about an acquaintance who actually uses two different names every day —his first name at home and his middle name at work—to help him keep his work "persona" from entering his home life. I don't begrudge anyone the techniques they need to manage their lives, but it seems to hint at a problematic notion of who we believe we need to be at work.

For example, generally speaking, it seems acceptable to bring ambition and pride to the workplace, as long as you're lowkey about it. But it's not okay, and in some settings it's even considered unprofessional, to bring a sense of love and compassion to work. Not all workplaces are like this, sure. But do a quick search online for tips on "professionalism," and you'll easily find a lot of advice on appearance and grooming but very little that pertains to being an authentic, whole person at work.

Even in the business discourse about digital transformation, talk is nothing without action. We have to be ready to accept the need for change, and it should come from a human-centered place. We have to be ready to habituate ourselves to the exponential changes that are coming, that are already happening, that will shake up our lives and force new perspective. And even if we do not embrace the change, we must learn to put humanity in the center of our efforts to move forward in the changed world in a holistic, integrative way.

---

[16] Kate O'Neill, "The Tech Humanist Manifesto," Medium.com, July 28, 2017, https://medium.com/intuitionmachine/the-tech-humanist-manifesto-bf9ebaa1e45f.

Tune in with empathy to anticipate what needs to change

B	**Be bold and honest** about the situation, even if it initially looks bleak
R	**Recognize** *what matters* (hint: this is *meaning*!)
I	**Identify** *what is going to matter* (hint: this is where *innovation* comes in!)
G	**Go all in on hope** as a tool of focus and refocus
H	**Habituate to change** (meaning: get used to it!)
T	**Tune in with empathy** to anticipate what needs to change
E	**Envision** bold ways forward
R	**Resolve** to work toward the best futures for the most people

We just talked about the need to habituate to change and transformation; in fact, you can think of change as the catalyst for adaptation. When big things are happening, adaptation is all about how you're allowing yourself to be nimble and loose, and adjusting the path you're on.

One of my favorite paired concepts is that of adaptation and empathy. It may be useful to think of adaptation as reactive and empathy as predictive. What I mean by that is when you think about adapting, you're *reacting* to the Change Factors around you. Empathy, on the other hand, helps you to *anticipate* the need for change. Empathy allows you to sort of sit with what other people are going to need, what's going to be important to others, and what matters to others. Empathy, when used well, can let you anticipate needs well before it's time to react to them.

Adaptability also lets you, as a leader, respond to changes in the market and what people as consumers are expecting from business. In the last few years, we've seen dramatic changes in the accountability people expect from brands when it comes to social justice and climate responsibility, for example. A company that wants to stay relevant and successful must bring authentic empathy into its soul-searching and strategic alignment to find room to improve elements of the product, the experience, or the company makeup itself to address what people perceive to be the shortcomings. But empathy could have shown us those needs from the beginning.

Empathizing with our fellow human beings in the world also reminds us about those who are suffering through climate disasters or who work in inhumane conditions. We must not create darker futures for other people while trying to create brighter futures for ourselves. The best futures for the most people, or bust. We're going to need all the adaptability we have to get there, and empathy will help us get ahead of what needs to change.

Envision bold ways forward

B	Be bold and honest about the situation, even if it initially looks bleak
R	Recognize *what matters* (hint: this is *meaning*!)
I	Identify *what is going to matter* (hint: this is where *innovation* comes in!)
G	Go all in on hope as a tool of focus and refocus
H	Habituate to change (meaning: get used to it!)
T	Tune in with empathy to anticipate what needs to change
E	Envision bold ways forward
R	Resolve to work toward the best futures for the most people

The Strategic Optimism Model starts with gaining clarity by looking candidly at our situation, whether in terms of collective global reality, our business strategy, or our personal lives, and then determining what is important, what will be important, and what we would most like to see happen.

But we also need to engage our imaginations fully, to conjure up ideas we can't yet put into words or visuals. We'll need to fumble around in the absence of an existing vocabulary, in the space where there aren't yet proven solutions, to suggest "what if?" ideas that may or may not be brilliant. We need to explore the fullness of what "envisioning" can do when it meets bold and fearless exploration.

Metaphors of vision

Picture this:

What we need is a way to live and lead that offers us not so frail a future as a flickering candle in a dark room but the sturdy glow of a lighthouse that, when we are lost, can guide us back to shore.

As human beings, we tend to visualize. Many of you when you read the sentence about flickering candles and glowing lighthouses were able to conjure illustrations of these objects in your mind's eye. Even people who were born blind nonetheless have the ability to experience some visual sensations in the brain.

It's a little funny that when we talk about the future—an abstract concept—we tend to talk in metaphors of what is perceivable to our eyes. We want to "look ahead," to "see" a "vision" of the future by "gazing into crystal balls," the results of which are sometimes "clear" but more often "unclear." So we end up "trying to see around corners" and "finding our way in the dark."

And of course, when we are hopeful about it, we talk about the future as being "bright."

Not only do we visualize, but also our brains form mental pictures in order to make sense of language and the world. We speak in metaphor and understand in visuals.

The right visuals, then, can spark our imagination and set our resolve. If we conjure the right images, we can align our resources, join forces, and change the fate of the world.

And the fate of the world could use some changing.

So with this book I have followed the English-language cultural convention and employed a set of visual metaphors: the *brightness* of the future, how well we can *see* into the future, the *foresight* of our actions, the *focus* of our efforts, the *clarity* of our resolve, the *horizon* of our vision in the distance, and so on. The opportunity for the solutions we create together goes well beyond this limited metaphor, but it's still useful to remember that this is how we relate to it.

In fact, here are a few related metaphors worth giving some thought to:

The metaphor of focus

When we talk about where we focus, or about problems requiring sharper focus, we're talking about needing to have the right problems or the right people in view.

This could mean we need to get closer to the issues, as we might do with an object we want to see better.

Some of these areas needing focus are social justice and racial justice, so getting closer might mean getting to know community stakeholders and inviting them to be part of the planning process.

The metaphor of distant vision

Being able to see far into the future is considered a special skill. If we are able to align ourselves toward solutions that are as yet unseen, we are, somewhat ironically, considered visionary. But that term tells us everything we need to know: The visionary is seeing and leading toward the solution on behalf of those who can't yet see it. That visionary could be you.

And what about the metaphor of brightness: Why a "bright" future?

Why do we even need the future to be bright? In an essay in her bestselling book *Men Explain Things to Me*, Rebecca Solnit quotes Virginia Woolf, who said, "The future is dark, which is the best thing the future can be, I think."[17] As Solnit goes on to write: "It's an extraordinary declaration, asserting that the unknown need not be turned into the known through false divination or the projection of grim political or ideological narratives; it's a celebration of darkness, willing—as that '*I think*' indicates—to be uncertain even about its own assertion." That's lovely and poetic, and I wanted to be sure to leave space here for Woolf and Solnit to have and express that view.

But we don't need false brightness, nor is false brightness particularly helpful to us. We never have to deceive ourselves into thinking an outcome is possible if deep down we believe it's not; we only have to calibrate our hopefulness toward the best possible outcome, and then recalibrate when the best possible outcomes change—which is why we must always try to move what's possible toward greater possibility.

In short, I can't say 100 percent for certain why for me, after *so much* reflection on the metaphors of vision and brightness and so much meta-analysis of their origins, the metaphor of brightness still rang true and made sense—except to say that in my own most hopeful vision of our collective fate, I can

---

[17] Rebecca Solnit, *Men Explain Things to Me* (Chicago: Haymarket Books, 2014), 86.

imagine our possible futures being illuminated by the glow of billions of individual searchlights pointed toward abundance, prosperity, and peace.

The Buddhist notion of the "luminous mind" may be instructive for us too. We can borrow the idea of thinking of brightness—or indeed optimism—as the state of enlightenment we reach when we *see things as they are*.

This approach requires a few things of us: namely, to start with, resilience. We must be willing to stare down hard truths without flinching and without losing spirit. It also demands an adaptable mind willing to update its thoughts to align with current realities.

One eye on now, one eye on the future

As leaders in business or in culture, we often have to think about what's happening right in front of us, *and* we simultaneously have to think about the far-off future.

I think a lot about when I worked in Netflix in its early years and how Reed Hastings led the company so brilliantly through a time of such big change. There we were in '99/2000 or so, still at that point engaged in an all-out bloody battle with Blockbuster, yet he was already diverting research and development funds into set-top boxes, which was the predecessor to streaming as we know it. This is years before we beat Blockbuster, and years before streaming would become the norm in people's homes. Reed was not satisfied with being the up-and-coming contender. He had one eye on *now*—on how to deal with what was right in front of him—*and* one eye looking off into the future. That balance perfectly demonstrates what it means to understand purpose, or what matters, and understand innovation, or what is going to matter.

Remember those two lenses as you're thinking about how to deal with what's right in front of you, and what you know you're going to need to deal with over time. The Change Factors we face demand that we approach them from this dualistic understanding of now and the future—of what matters and what is going to matter.

Resolve to work towards the best futures for the most people

B	**Be bold and honest** about the situation, even if it initially looks bleak
R	**Recognize** *what matters* (hint: this is *meaning*!)
I	**Identify** *what is going to matter* (hint: this is where *innovation* comes in!)
G	**Go all in on hope** as a tool of focus and refocus
H	**Habituate to change** (meaning: get used to it!)
T	**Tune in with empathy** to anticipate what needs to change
E	**Envision** bold ways forward
R	**Resolve** to work toward the best futures for the most people

In my last book, *Tech Humanist*, I used the phrase "the best futures for the most people" twenty-seven times. (Looks like I'm on track to break that record in this book.) Clearly, the phrase means something to me. While *meaning* as a central facet of the human condition is the intellectual core of my body of work, the beating heart of my work is having genuine opportunities—through helping leaders rethink their approach to strategy, alignment, community, experience, and technology—to actually witness movements toward the best futures for the most people.

At the core of this idea of "helping humanity prepare for an increasingly tech-driven future" is a recognition that the tech-driven future dovetails with other issues, such as the climate crisis and the spread of misinformation. But how do we actually get from repeating the phrase as a mantra to truly making a difference? Can any of us *actually* help bring about the best futures for the most people? And how does Strategic Optimism help us to do this?

A few years ago I met Manav Subodh, who runs 1M1B, or 1 Million for 1 Billion[18]—a youth leadership program in India. His program encourages young people in villages and towns all over India to develop programs and products that can improve the lives of a hundred people, and then a thousand. They learn about solving human problems at scale in approachable terms. Some of the young leaders create social programs focused on elder care, refugees, young women who want better educational opportunities, and so on. Some create valuable software, such as a program to help farmers manage their inventory at market. Each year, a few dozen of the most promising of these leaders get to come with him to the United Nations headquarters in New York to speak at the annual 1M1B youth summit, which is where I met Manav. I have been privileged to speak with his young cohorts several times since.

We often talk about preparing for the worst and hoping for the best, which means all our active attention is given to the negative outcomes while we passively await the best outcomes. As I discuss in detail in The Strategic Optimism Model: How We Can Harness Our Human Superpowers, I believe that's more or less the inverse of what we need to do. We need to acknowledge the full range of possible outcomes, including all of the possible negatives *and* all the possible positives. We do need to mitigate the risks and manage the harms of our intended actions, but our usual approach falls down when we don't direct even *more* of our energy and effort into realizing the positive outcomes. Hoping the best will happen is not a strategy either.

For whom?

Now is our chance to center voices that have not historically been centered: e.g., Indigenous populations on social justice issues and their approaches to environmental protection and sustainability; Black Americans in matters of racial injustice; women in discussions of nonviolence and radical progress; etc. An easy move is to involve affected communities earlier in design considerations when new projects begin. As we are reminded in this quote from

---

[18] https://www.activate1m1b.org/

Indian futurist Anab Jain: "Those with the least power to shape the future often suffer its worst consequences[19]."

We must push ourselves beyond our comfort. The challenge is that people who are used to systemic privilege—and I am aware that I experience many, many forms of privilege myself—are too often afraid of what the world will look like *for them* once there is greater equality and equity for all.

It's a protectionist stance rather than a belief in abundance, that there is enough for all of us to flourish. If we were really committed to the idea that no one should need suffer for another person to thrive, we would pursue that ideal in small ways and large ways, across all aspects of living.

We have all benefited for too long from the suffering of other humans. As Kathryn Yusoff writes in *A Billion Black Anthropocenes or None*: "The movement of energy between enslaved bodies in plantations, plants, long-dead fossilized plants, and industrialized labor is a geochemical equation of extraction in the conversion of surplus."[20]

We have a tremendous opportunity to decolonize our way of thinking about land, place, people, societies. (With credit to the work of Ngugi wa Thiong'o for the richness and importance of the concept of decolonization as relates to language, thinking, and cultural influence.)

Now is our chance to move toward a more just and equitable world—a more just and equitable city, state, country, planet.

These opportunities are vitally important when we think about emerging technologies like artificial intelligence. As AI criminologist Renée Cummings said when she was a guest on the *Tech Humanist Show*:

"What AI also needs is more diverse stakeholder engagement. So far we've been designing technologies that revictimize and remarginalize communities, when you're thinking about the deployment of surveillance technologies into a disinvested community. What we do need is to

---

[19] Anab Jain, "How Will We Live?," Oct 20, 2015. https://medium.com/@anabjain/how-will-we-live-d9baf00acac9

[20] Kathryn Yusoff, *A Billion Black Anthropocenes or None* (Minneapolis: University of Minnesota Press, 2018), 16.

educate people in communities on all these technologies that are being used against them. They need to understand the kind of digital force that's now being applied against them…

"What we really need to do is democratize this technology so people in communities understand how their data could be weaponized against them. People need to understand the power of their data. This is why data advocacy is so important because data is a part of your civil rights."[21]

This extension of equity and justice needs to apply to the built environment, as well, with planning that takes into consideration the needs of people with varying mobility issues and disabilities. A space is only meaningful to the public to the extent that it genuinely includes the whole public; too many of the features designed in cities and buildings are ableist and exclusionary.

Our best futures must include the most people, which means designing with diverse stakeholders and including a wide range of perspectives in the deployment of new technologies, programs, spaces, and solutions. Without that true inclusion, we will still be mired in the shortcomings of past failures to create equity. Our bold visions must be broad enough to be shared.

---

[21] Kate O'Neill, "Episode 10 - Renée Cummings," September 25, 2020, in *Tech Humanist Show with Kate O'Neill*, produced by Kate O'Neill, podcast, MP3 audio, https://www.thetechhumanist.com/2020/09/25/the-tech-humanist-show-episode-10-renee-cummings/.

Chapter 3:

Playing to Humanity's Strengths

WE HUMANS ARE WIRED A certain way. On some counts we share characteristics with other animals, like being curious and creative, and like animals, we use tools to solve problems. (Ever seen a fish toss a mollusk against a rock to break the shell? We can all agree that's cool. Unless you're the mollusk.) We even arguably share traits with machines; humans and machines alike try to find the least resource-consuming way to do things—which you could also describe as the laziest way. And I mean no disrespect by that! Lazy techniques are generally more efficient techniques.

But even though we have all of these traits in common with nonhuman animals and machines, in other ways, we are totally our own creatures.

People often think of human tendencies as selfish and destructive, and we all embody those traits now and then to greater or lesser degrees. But when the cards are stacked against us, case study after case study has continually shown that humans tend to outperform our expectations and help one another. The sociology professor Lee Clarke found that during the events of September 11, 2001, at the World Trade Center, people did not tend to panic and act irrationally; instead, the circumstances created what he termed "a sense of 'we-ness'" among those threatened.[22] Rebecca Solnit's book *Hope in the Dark* examines human behavior in the aftermath of disaster and finds "in fact, in most disasters most people are calm, resourceful, altruistic, and creative."[23] And in *Humankind: A Hopeful History*, Rutger Bregman writes: "Catastrophes bring out the best in people. I know of no other sociological finding that's backed by so much solid evidence that's so blithely ignored. The picture we're fed by the media is consistently the opposite of what happens when disaster strikes."[24]

Besides being basically decent animals who are, at worst, underestimated, we are the only species (as far as we know) who is self-aware enough to ponder our own existence. That's a big deal because our ponderings have inspired centuries of culture and philosophy that are all part of what we know as civilization.

We are aware of ourselves, and aware of our place in the larger community of human beings, and the even larger community of humanity throughout history.

"And you realize that in a very real sense we're meant for a very profound complementarity. It is the nature of things. You don't have to be a believer in anything. I mean I could not speak as I am speaking without having learned it from other human beings. I could not walk as a human being. I could not think as a human being, except through learning it from other human beings. I learned to be a human being from other human beings. We belong in this delicate network. It is actually quite profound."

---

[22] American Sociological Association, "In Disasters, Panic Is Rare; Altruism Dominates," ScienceDaily, August 8, 2002, https://www.sciencedaily.com/releases/2002/08/020808075321.htm

[23] Solnit, *Hope in the Dark*, xvii.

[24] Rutger Bregman, *Humankind: A Hopeful History*, trans. Elizabeth Manton and Erica Moore (New York: Little Brown, 2020), 6.

— Archbishop Desmond Tutu in *The Book of Joy: Lasting Happiness in a Changing World* by Dalai Lama, Desmond Tutu, et al.[25]

That multidimensional awareness underlies a lot of what motivates and moves us in ways that don't stem from pure survival instinct as an organism. That awareness informs our sense of ethics and morality, and connects us to the past as well as the future.

In applying Strategic Optimism, we need to play to humanity's strengths. Some of these strengths overlap with what the model calls for, but others are important to acknowledge on their own.

[25] Lama, Dalai, et al. The Book of Joy: Lasting Happiness in a Changing World. United Kingdom, Penguin Publishing Group, 2016. p.60

The Human Superpowers Mindset Toolkit

The tools we most need to face the Change Factors of the future with optimism and determination are, amazingly, traits most humans already have in abundance. That means you! You already have the powers you need; you just need to recognize them and use them intentionally.

I like to think of these traits as our Human Superpowers. They're built in, they adapt, they allow us to face incredible challenges with strength and cooperation—traits like:

Both/and, or the ability to think integratively and hold conflicting truths at the same time. We'll dig into this in the following pages.

Empathy and adaptation, which in combination give us perceptive and reactive abilities to deal with change. We'll also dig into these shortly.

Our orientation toward **meaning**, which not only is part of the Strategic Optimism ("BRIGHTER") model we've already discussed, but also is really our core Human Superpower.

In addition to these, we have helpful traits including:

Courage. It's brave to allow yourself to hope. Whether you hope for something personal, in the realm of romance, or something professional, like a promotion, or if you feel hope about big issues like the climate—any of these situations are full of unknowns and things beyond your control. That means they can be scary to think about, so you get extra credit for feeling any hope at all.

But here's the thing: While it's brave to merely hope, it takes real *courage* to apply that hope to action.

The world needs your audacious hope, your bold vision, your clear-eyed plans, and your determined actions to follow through. It takes courage to make that happen. I see you.

We also have:

Cooperation and teamwork. As I pulled together stories of organizations and cities confronting their challenges and developing plans to overcome them, a common theme in them was *collective action*. You can see this readily through the kind of teamwork we see in sports (perhaps as romanticized in TV shows like *Ted Lasso*) or through the collaboration we see across the arts (what would Oates be without Hall?). Cooperation drives labor unions, voting blocs, boycotts, mission-based organizations, and other group efforts to try to influence outcomes in favor of workers, citizens, consumers, and people in general. You may think of examples that don't align with your priorities or values, per se, but you should nonetheless recognize the tool for what it is, and the human trait for what it is.

On a personal level and a professional level, our Human Superpowers can genuinely help us cope with changes and see ways forward from them. And the best way forward is to apply these Human Superpowers to create the best futures for the most people.

Both/And: Our Human Superpower of integrative thinking

In its broadest sense, technology is applied knowledge. Any animal that has figured out how to smash shells with a certain kind of rock has mastered the basics. But technology as we've come to know it in the internet age—the ever-present computer-calculated, data-interconnected world of digital knowledge and digital experiences—is rock-smashing at a whole different level. And so far, it's unique to humans. As a human achievement, it's an extension of our humanity. And humanity isn't all virtue and honor; there's a lot of brutality, a lot of backstabbing, and a lot of base instinct at play throughout human history.

But the kinds of technology we are developing now, the kinds that bring with them capacity and scale, require us to be on our best behavior. No intellectual laziness allowed.

So am I optimistic or pessimistic about the future of AI and automation for human experiences?

Both. I'm optimistic that tech can still serve us if we deploy it well. And I'm doubtful about how beneficial those decisions will be if they are governed only by profit motives—which is why we need an integrative way of looking at the future.

Think of both/and thinking as being intellectually ambidextrous.

We have to pay attention to the events of the present *and* think about how the present trends might influence the direction of the future. We need to be able to think about the tremendous opportunities of tech, such as voice assistants, *and* think about how the constant surveillance in our homes changes what we need from privacy laws. Simplistic, reductive thinking is not a tool that prepares us for the future ahead of us.

We need to be able to operate just as easily from either orientation. After all, our brains do have two lobes and while the majority of right vs. left brain dominance is a myth[26], some of our tasks are indeed localized to certain regions of the brain[27]. This implies less about whether you're innately logical or creative and more about how much power there is in using all of your capabilities together (and even reinforces the value of collective intelligence). The ability to use our full complement of reactions and reasoning—emotional, rational, fearful, hopeful, short-term, long-term, etc—can help us make complex decisions, often in an instant. But recognizing both the bad and the good possibilities is only the beginning. The trick to Strategic Optimism is: We need to lean into the work we know it will take to achieve the positive outcomes.

In one example of corporate leadership toward a better future, in 2010 Unilever CEO Paul Polman launched the Unilever Sustainable Living Plan (USLP). The aim was to double the size of the business by 2020 while both improving the health and well-being of more than a billion people and halving the company's environmental impact. The company follows that direction even today, more than two years after the end of Polman's tenure as CEO.

Unilever states their purpose this way: "to make sustainable living commonplace."[28] And part of the way that must be achieved is by building sustainability into the supply chain and business operations. Sustainability can't be pushed off to consumers to bear the burden of sacrifice and complexity.

However, on January 21, 2021, they announced efforts to diversify their supply chain and improve working conditions, and the stock price promptly took a nosedive.

You and I may agree that these are efforts the world should be supporting, but we also know the stock market can be skittish about change. The single-minded stock market should not be the deciding vote on what priorities are pursued by what is increasingly the most influential class of entity: the corporation. Business leaders looking to move us forward will have to gird their loins for nervous reactions, acting with confidence that investors will often react positively once the market reacts positively.

---

[26] TIME, "There Is No Left Brain/Right Brain Divide," Stephen M. Kosslyn and G. Wayne Miller, November 29, 2013. https://ideas.time.com/2013/11/29/there-is-no-left-brainright-brain-divide/

[27] NPR, "The Truth About The Left Brain / Right Brain Relationship," Tania Lombrozo, December 2, 2013. https://www.npr.org/sections/13.7/2013/12/02/248089436/the-truth-about-the-left-brain-right-brain-relationship

[28] https://www.unilever.com/about/who-we-are/our-strategy/

The economy is people, as I assert elsewhere (head over to the section on The Economy Is People for further exploration of that idea), which means that for businesses to flourish, they should be led in a human-affirming way.

The table below offers a few different ways to conceptualize the differences between a limiting, either/or mindset and an expansive both/and mindset. Some of the metaphors may make more sense to you than others, but I hope at least one gives you a little "Aha!" moment that helps connect the power of integrative thinking with the opportunities ahead of us.

	Either/Or Thinking	Both/And Thinking
	Black-and-white	Shades of gray (or grey)
	Scarcity	Abundance
	Separate	Integrative
Tend toward	Reductionist	Nuanced
	Restricted	Expansive
Are things complex?	Simplistic	Multifaceted
What is true?	Rigid perception of what is true	Multiple things can be true at once
	Exclusionary	Inclusive
Measures of success	Narrowly-focused; profit or growth only; oblivious to ecosystem impact	Holistic; community-focused; ecosystem-minded
	Single metric histogram	Ecosystem health dashboard

How do you apply this? In solving problems, in your organization, in your day-to-day life, look for opportunities to challenge reductive, either/or thinking when you find yourself defaulting to it. Try asking: What else matters here? What might I have overlooked?

Think about the implications of the controversial study from researchers at Northeastern University[29] that suggested reports of violent crime in Boston increased in areas with more Airbnb listings. While Airbnb strenuously took issue with the study and its findings, what the findings suggest, if even partially true, is not that the rentals per se, or the tourism, or the tourists, lead directly to violent crime; instead, the findings suggest that people in a community become increasingly disconnected when the residential units become short-term rentals.[30] It *almost* doesn't matter how valid the study's findings turn out to be across multiple markets; there's insight to be gleaned just in the overall idea. Both perspectives inherent in this controversy can say something worth considering and applying to analogous situations: both that short-term rentals in a neighborhood offer a helpful service to travelers who want to experience living like a local, *and* that short-term rentals can crowd out longer-term residents in a neighborhood—particularly in gentrifying neighborhoods that are already pricing out longer-term lower-income residents—and leave it without a healthy social fabric.

Is it true? Probably yes and no. Is it meaningful? It could be. As an illustration it offers directional guidance about how to build products and solutions that mesh better with community, that solve one set of problems without causing another.

Thinking this way requires a nimble mind, but Strategic Optimism is, in its own way, an inherent contradiction. The best paths forward are going to take some integrative, complex thinking.

---

[29] PLOS ONE, "Airbnb and neighborhood crime: The incursion of tourists or the erosion of local social dynamics?" Laiyang Ke,
Daniel T. O'Brien,
Babak Heydari, 2021. https://journals.plos.org/plosone/article?id=10.1371/journal.pone.0253315

[30] Boston.com, "Increases in Airbnb listings linked to more violent crime in Boston neighborhoods, Northeastern study suggests," Mihiro Shimano, July 23, 2021. https://www.boston.com/news/local-news/2021/07/23/increases-in-airbnb-listings-linked-to-more-violent-crime-in-boston-neighborhoods-study-suggests/

Beyond "Dystopia versus Utopia"

Among the reasons why many of us find the future scary to contemplate is because science fiction and literature tend to give us one lens to view it through: the dichotomy of *dystopia* versus *utopia*. It's nearly always broken down that way: either/or.

On top of that, realistically, I suspect you'll agree with me that most of us understand socially that we're not really even supposed to talk about utopia in any earnest way; after all, no one really believes that everything will go exactly right or that we'll ever be living in a perfect world. That future is *not* happening, which takes half of the dichotomy out of the equation. Then all we are are left with is a dystopian future—at best, greater or lesser degrees of dystopia. The only vocabulary that remains to conceive of and plan for the future is *how* dystopian a new thing feels.

It's hard to insist on better when we don't have a shared vision of the future we want, yet the default mode of talking about the future is so lacking in nuance.

In my work around the impact of emerging technology on the future of human experiences, I have learned that I am often perceived as something of an optimist. A few years ago as I was being booked to speak at a conference, the organizers were deciding whether I should be the opening or closing keynote. The other keynote speaker was someone whose work was very heavy and troubling, but no less important—so I learned from the organizers that they envisioned my work as the antidote or counterweight to the heaviness of her message. As soon as I understood that, I considered it my duty to anchor the possibility of better futures but also to create the intellectual space for the candor needed to recognize the current reality so we can build on it.

I'm fine with being thought of as an optimist, but I want to make sure it's understood that optimism, for me, is not about seeing everything as already bright and perfect like the utopia we all agree can't exist; it's about seeing the *potential* for brightness and letting strategy guide us to work our way there.

There is no utopia, but...

Utopia as a future construct is just as limiting as dystopia, but looking around for glimpses at what pseudo-utopia might be is a pretty interesting exercise.

Is democracy a kind of utopia? In its best form, it errs on the side of collective action, combined efforts, supporting one another, and holding power accountable to the people. That's a pretty amazing and human-centric set of ideals. It doesn't work out that way in practice most of the time, but that doesn't mean it isn't instructive to think about in its best form.

Even biology offers a glimpse of pseudo-utopia if you look at it from a certain angle. We live on a planet where the best-adapted attributes flourish, and to put it in Jeff Goldblum terms, life finds a way[31]. We can draw inspiration from that, surely, without applying it too literally (or letting it lull us into an ill-conceived theme park for dinosaurs that is clearly *not* utopian).

The point is, just as we have been told again and again that "hope is not a strategy" and that optimism is unserious and unintellectual, perhaps keeping utopia in our pockets as a thought exercise is still useful now and then, if only to help us to envision those bold and bright future worlds we can build.

Add myopia to the mix

In addition to the limited framework of dystopia versus utopia, there's another limiting lens we need to acknowledge: myopia. The limitations of dystopia versus utopia may lie in our own myopia as human beings.

We have a tendency to be too nearsighted, to make only short-term decisions, to think only a short distance ahead instead of considering our impact on a scale of exponential growth and a time horizon of decades or centuries. But the choices we make in the present will determine the future that we are destined to live in. This means we must look beyond this year's perspective— this moment's perspective—and toward the decade we're already on course to shaping. There we must lay out a plan for change, for effect, for impact.

Every so often, we need to make time to challenge ourselves to think big: How are we going to ensure our work, our businesses, our technologies align

---

[31] https://knowyourmeme.com/memes/life-uh-finds-a-way

with solving the world's greatest challenges? How are we going to make an impact in our communities and beyond our communities?

Only by giving ourselves the time and permission to think beyond the present moment will we have the perspective to find the alignment our work can have with the solutions humanity needs.

The truth in inherent contrasts

There's just something so appealing about inherent contrasts and contradictions.

My last book, *Tech Humanist* (a title filled with contrast), dealt with how business could work toward digital transformation that integrates technology for more successful business objectives while also improving human experiences. The book before that, *Pixels and Place*, was about the integration of online and offline experiences through our personal data.

The trend goes back even further: Some years ago I had a company called [meta]marketer. Years before that, I started a blog called "Corporate Idealist, " dedicated to the idea that business could be a creative and meaningful endeavor. (I got to interview exemplary leaders like Tony Hsieh, CEO of Zappos.)

You get the idea. I share all this here because it demonstrates, beyond my weakness for silly wordplay, that I believe in the inherent insight—and sometimes surprising truth—that can come from deep consideration of opposing ideas in juxtaposition. It's related to both/and thinking: forcing near-opposites together creates a tension—a healthy and illustrative one.

Certainly this is one reason why Strategic Optimism appeals to me, but in my professional experience I have genuinely found that optimism is an important and oft overlooked part of future-ready strategy—in the sense that without it, leaders can too easily adopt the status quo mentality and not visualize the better outcomes they could work toward.

In fact, we hold ourselves back in many ways with the kind of limited thinking that doesn't include both optimism and strategy. Here are just a few examples:

Holding ourselves back from being prepared for success: Let's say you're launching a product, and it gets picked up by a national retailer—like a new snack getting into Whole Foods. Are you prepared for that success? Scaling up to meet that kind of demand can make or break a small business. You've probably spent months, if not years, thinking of everything that could go wrong in production, but has your preparation given you the chance to think about *what could go right*?

Holding ourselves back from taking our work further: Or perhaps you've set annual goals for your business in terms of revenue or new customers or deals closed. Do your goals reflect your hope for what you can achieve? Sure, hope alone isn't enough to get the deals done, but if you aren't bringing *any* sense of hope to your strategic planning, you may be settling for less than the opportunities that are really out there.

Scaling biases, cultural weirdnesses, and other consequences: In software and beyond, sometimes the agile development cycle encourages us to make guesses and assumptions as we build so we can get done and get to market. That way you can find out how people respond to your product in real life and in real time. But it's also how, in far too many cases, background decisions that aren't thought through get left in place as a product reaches mass market adoption. Maybe you launched an app, perhaps a dating app, and the app was received so well and so quickly it seemed like there was no time to go back and adjust the data model so it was less biased (toward non-heterosexual people, for instance) or reword the onboarding questions so they're more inclusive.

Or, to cite a specific example of a different kind, say you're in charge of Peloton, the exercise equipment company, and your products skyrocket in popularity during a global pandemic when most people are more or less confined to their homes. But when the US Consumer Product Safety Commission claims that the Tread+ machines are linked to dozens of injuries among children and pets—plus the death of a child—rather than forfeit momentum, you dig in and resist. Then you are forced to make a public apology and conduct a massive recall, resulting in plans for software improvements that will automatically lock the Tread+ after use and require a four-digit passcode to unlock it...all of which could've been done from the beginning or earlier if your leaders had considered what success on this scale might really look like—specifically, a place where mass market adoption would demand children and pets being critical subjects of the conversations about safety.[32]

---

[32] "Peloton Recalls Treadmills After Injuries and a Child's Death," The New York Times (nytimes.com), https://www.nytimes.com/2021/05/05/business/peloton-recall-tread-plus.html

The best time to work out those details is at the beginning, by including diverse contributors, community stakeholders, and reviewers who can challenge insular thinking. But even if your product already has scale, there's no time like the present to review and audit for inclusion. Start building a more diverse and inclusive team from today forward.

The value of holding opposing ideas

I'm not the only one to think there's value in this. More than sixty years ago, F. Scott Fitzgerald saw "the ability to hold two opposed ideas in mind at the same time, and still retain the ability to function" as "the test of a first-rate intelligence."[33] He wrote further, "One should, for example, be able to see that things are hopeless and yet be determined to make them otherwise." Quite an apt description of Strategic Optimism, don't you think?

Likewise, in his book *The Opposable Mind*, Roger Martin explores the problem-solving power of "integrative thinking" by examining more than fifty management success stories such as The Four Seasons, Proctor & Gamble, and eBay. It demonstrated "how, like the opposable thumb, the 'opposable mind'—Martin's term for the human brain's ability 'to hold two conflicting ideas in constructive tension'—is an intellectually advantageous evolutionary leap through which decision-makers can synthesize 'new and superior ideas.'"

Finally, one of the formative references in my work comes from the business classic *Good to Great*[34]—what Jim Collins calls the Stockdale Paradox[35]: the idea that a blend of brutal reality along with hope is the perfect combination for overcoming adversity in situations ranging from market turbulence to being a prisoner of war.

Taken together, all of this suggests that one way for us to push ahead to the best, most evolved versions of ourselves is to challenge ourselves to take what appear to be contradictions and hold them, consider them, and find the possible truths that may be hiding in the *bothness* of them.

---

[33] Esquire, "The Crack-Up," F. Scott Fitzgerald. https://www.esquire.com/lifestyle/a4310/the-crack-up/

[34] Collins, Jim. Good to Great. Random House Business Books, 2001.

[35] https://www.jimcollins.com/concepts/confront-the-brutal-facts.html

Resisting reductive thinking

Every day our interactions and transactions online are increasingly tracked, aggregated, analyzed, optimized, and monetized. And the result is that the experiences available to us both online and offline are increasingly determined by data and finessed by algorithms. What we do in the world—on social media, in stores, through email, and so on—creates a vast pool of data and a kind of feedback loop, and that data then gets used to further shape the experiences offered to us and others. In this manner our individual worlds are becoming ever more refined but also ever more conformed to our worldviews, our biases, and the preferences we have expressed and not expressed. We have to keep pushing against the oversimplification of our lives even as we benefit from the conveniences this affords us.

Yet most of this is neither inherently good nor inherently bad.

What if I were to ask you, "How do you feel about algorithms determining human experiences?" If the first thing you think of is any kind of algorithm that makes entertainment recommendations for you like Netflix, Spotify, or Pandora, who present you with curated options for what you will likely enjoy watching or listening to, you would probably say your algorithmic experiences have been good. You probably learned about new music, or maybe rediscovered beloved old music you haven't heard in a while. You might think that's a perfect experience. That's exactly what I want algorithms to do. I want them to observe my behaviors and the behaviors of people like me, and then show me what is good so I don't have to spend all my time on discovery and potentially missing out on something I might like. Maybe your feeling toward algorithms is that simple: "Hey, this is all wonderful. This is utopia."

However, if I asked you, "How do you feel about algorithms determining human experiences?" and the first thing you think about is criminal justice, your feelings will likely be very different. Perhaps you're thinking about the data that goes into those systems and the algorithms that have been encoded in ways that produce racist and discriminatory results. You're considering how algorithms are applied to criminal justice and the law, and you're aware of the studies that have shown the racist and otherwise prejudiced, biased ways in which those algorithms disproportionately implicate young Black men and Black defendants.

(There are plenty of studies around that, after all, and we'll look at some topics related to algorithmic bias in Chapter 13: The Opportunity for Human-Centric Tech and Innovation.) If that's where your mind goes when I bring up algorithmic experiences, then you're probably concluding that algorithms determining human experience is dystopia.

And this is where I think we come to a fork in the road with this whole dystopia versus utopia lens. We've come right back around to the uselessness of that dichotomy because algorithms determining human experiences cannot be both dystopia and utopia at the same time. Or maybe it can. That lens is useless to us, so we need to embrace the power of *both*. And we need to be able to integrate our thinking and recognize that both of those things are true in some way. It's true that algorithms can be used to make sense of the world around you and present you with relevant experiences, *and* it's true that algorithms can overstep what they are really prepared to offer, implicate innocent people, and make life very unpleasant for people who are pushed to the margins of society. Those things are both true. We have to deal with the bothness of that and the trueness of both of those ideas.

Systems thinking—putting something into the context of a larger whole— may not save us from the hazards we face, but reductive thinking will almost certainly ruin us. We're bound to be better off, in almost every case, taking an integrative, systems-thinking approach to solving human problems at scale because they're too big to be reduced to simply either good or bad.

Empathy and adaptation: the twin Human Superpowers of change

Some kinds of technology provide an opportunity for us to make use of two more Human Superpowers—specifically, the powerful combination of adaptation and empathy.

Empathy gives us the insight to recognize harms, to know when something is causing someone pain. But we can also use empathy to anticipate what needs to change.

Adaptation is the skill we've developed to voluntarily accept change. While adapting is something all living things do, the human capacity for adaptation is something more. Because we have higher reasoning, we can see the need for change coming then get ahead of it if we have the will. My favorite people in the world have all reinvented themselves through their careers and their lifestyles many times over, sensing and following their instincts to seek out new challenges and new opportunities.

Life at its most fundamental is entirely consistent with adaptation. Nature reinvents itself regularly with what you might call—if you were trying to illustrate a point—something like optimism.

Adaptation is also a key theme in global climate action discourse, as activists increasingly highlight the need for resilience measures (such as seawalls, water-permeable pavements, etc.) to help people and regions reduce their vulnerability by preparing for the existing and anticipated impacts caused by rising temperatures. While in recent history the discussion of climate has focused on mitigation efforts, and these are critically important, we're at the point where the real-life impacts are already happening and more are on their way, so the shift toward adaptation is key to our survival.

This theme of resilience is relevant beyond climate mitigation too; you can think of it as applying to companies, to cities, and to us as individuals.

Resilience is what we gain as we empower ourselves to adapt to the changes we face.

Empathy and adaptation are also important concepts in technology.

Over the last decade there's been an increasing amount of talk about empathy in design, in technology, and especially, in virtual experience. Some examples and studies have focused on virtual reality used in journalism and storytelling as a great tool for empathy, as it allows people to put themselves in other places, such as in war-torn areas or amid racially biased encounters. While these scenarios can help people who participate in them begin to understand some of the issues involved, they are not perfect substitutes for *lived* experience. As Kaitlin Ugolik Phillips, the author of *The Future of Feeling: Building Empathy in a Tech-Obsessed World*, pointed out when she was a guest on the *Tech Humanist Show*: "When it comes to virtual reality experiences that are meant to build empathy, it can be so easy to say 'okay this is an empathy-building experience—put on the headset, pretend to be someone else,' just end it there, and now this person walks away with this idea that they know what it's like to have a disability or to live in a different skin color."[36]

Kaitlin went on to clarify that what these experiences do well, or what they should really be used for, is highlighting the gap in experience. She's right, of course. Our limited exposure to experiencing life in a state different from the one we normally inhabit only gives us a glimpse, not the full story. And that recognition is itself a form of empathy.

In terms of how adaptation applies to technology, we can look toward the exciting area of biomimicry. For example, one of the more readily apparent benefits to humans from the study of biomimicry is the advancement of prosthetics that function more like natural limbs. This again is about responding to change.

Biomimicry is also big in the construction field, where innovators borrow the use of forms and strategies and the development of materials that are more adaptable to environmental conditions and conserve natural resources. Interior designs inspired by nature that allow for access to sunlight, for example, can

---

[36] Kate O'Neill, "Episode 6 – Kaitlin Ugolik Phillips," August 28, 2020, in Tech Humanist Show with Kate O'Neill, produced by Kate O'Neill, podcast, MP3 audio, https://www.thetechhumanist.com/2020/08/28/the-tech-humanist-show-episode-6-kaitlin-ugolik-phillips/.

reduce the energy demand for artificial light while improving quality of life.[37] Some developers are even thinking about ecosystem-level biomimicry that incorporates regenerative design for urban environments.[38]

Neural networks in machine learning are influenced conceptually by human and other kinds of intelligence observed throughout nature, and that inspiration will no doubt continue in the field of artificial intelligence.

---

[37] Rasha Mahmoud Ali El-Zeiny, "Biomimicry as a Problem Solving Methodology in Interior Architecture," Procedia - Social and Behavioral Sciences, Volume 50, 2012, Pages 502-512,
https://doi.org/10.1016/j.sbspro.2012.08.054.
https://www.sciencedirect.com/science/article/pii/S1877042812031928
[38] Blanco, E.; Pedersen Zari, M.; Raskin, K.; Clergeau, P. Urban Ecosystem-Level Biomimicry and Regenerative Design: Linking Ecosystem Functioning and Urban Built Environments. Sustainability 2021, 13, 404. https://doi.org/10.3390/su13010404

Dealing with the negative side of human experience

Of course, we have human traits that *aren't* superpowers too. (Human kryptonite?) Some of the characteristics that make us most human are also the ones that are hard to deal with, that leave us feeling overwhelmed or frightened, and that leave us rationalizing our way out of doing anything to change our circumstances.

We also know that suffering exists in the world, and it can be hard to look at. That, as well, might prevent us from making the changes we need to make.

We need to give ourselves the grace to recognize these traits and work with them and around them. We need a plan—a strategy, one might say—for handling our inner objections and resistance. Let's dig into a few of these ideas and what to do about them.

What traits are at odds with Strategic Optimism?

Of course, not all of our human traits are productive and positive, as I'm sure you well know. In fact, some of the traits common in humans *don't* play well with Strategic Optimism, and it behooves us to call them out and put them in check so we can proceed with the work we need to do. Namely:

Pessimism. Some people tend to focus on the worst in every situation. In fact, some people seek out the worst. While it's important to have a full awareness of the harms and risks of any given scenario, dwelling on what could go wrong doesn't get us where we most want to go.

Acknowledging whatever harsh realities exist as well as the gravest risks, harms, and possible outcomes makes up an important first step of Strategic Optimism, but the picture is very much incomplete without including the brighter side of the spectrum: the work already in progress that we can build on, the inclusive actions we can take to develop equity and justice, the innovations we might make to leap us forward. By defaulting to only those worst ideas, believing them to be inevitable, framing your thinking and language and plans around them are all the very opposite actions of what will lead us forward the way we most hope.

Cynicism. There's a paradox in culture of increased levels of cynicism yet also increased credulity in what we consume on our feeds and through our chosen sources. Both trends are evidence of a lack of critical thinking and commitment to the best outcomes.

Hope requires commitment, and that takes bravery. To be cynical, on the other hand, is to admit defeat—except it's inherently insincere because it's like admitting defeat without having the courage to admit that you're admitting defeat. Cynicism is greatly at odds with Strategic Optimism. It's a cop-out.

Cynicism is an easy way to avoid responsibility for the work the future needs. Sure, it would be far easier to abdicate responsibility for clear-eyed planning, for reinventing systems, for rethinking priorities, for reallocating resources—yet what we desperately need instead are people brave enough to double down on what we hope and hedge just enough against what we fear. While an optimistic view of the future can allow us to envision bold new ways forward, the cynic's detachment doesn't offer anything new.

Denial. Denial is expensive! It wastes the precious time we could be using to deal with the challenges we face. And it costs us clarity, obstructing from us the perspective we need to pursue the best solutions. We simply can't afford to deny the Change Factors in our lives and in our world.

Denial is often understood to be part of the grieving process before the new reality of our situation sets in. But in my own experiences with significant loss, I have found that shock and denial are two very different experiences: When you first begin to accept the enormity of a loss, it may overwhelm your mind and dull your senses. That shock is usually temporary, and may be a necessary adaptation to move forward through the loss. Denial, on the other hand, gets in the way. Whether you're grappling with a worldwide catastrophe, a business disappointment, or a personal sorrow, denial will not help you accept or process the loss or pain of those difficult situations, and we need to let ourselves do that to make room for the future. The sooner we can free ourselves from avoiding the truth of our circumstances, the sooner we may begin to plan a hopeful path forward.

What is not at odds with Strategic Optimism, though?

On the other hand, some traits you might think of as being in tension with optimism generally are perfectly at home with Strategic Optimism.

Healthy skepticism. It's natural to suspect that something could go wrong or that we don't have all the answers. Skepticism is not the same as denial, provided it's accompanied by curiosity and a desire to learn the truth.

Curiosity. A genuine kind of wondering is always healthy. What happens *if*, *why* is this the way it is...anything curiosity leads us to investigate in the name of creating better futures is probably moving us in the right direction.

Planning. We're not going to sit around and hope! The "strategic" part of Strategic Optimism is all about planning. We need to embrace our own agency and our responsibility to make things happen.

How does a Strategic Optimist think about suffering?

It can seem at odds with a hopeful view to recognize that people do suffer, and that pain is inevitable. But pain is natural. We cannot avoid pain, even if we wish to—and who wouldn't wish to avoid pain?

Suffering, however, we have an opportunity to limit. Suffering, after all, is pain experienced at some kind of scale: by a great many people, or by people over a long time, or just pain felt very deeply.

Even though we know that pain is natural and unavoidable, we must open our eyes to the suffering of people. We know we suffer, and we know others suffer as well.

Here are two complementary ideas worth noting:

The first is: **We can work to alleviate some amount of human suffering.**

We know the climate crisis will cause human suffering. In fact, it already does. We know people will experience more frequent droughts, famines, and severe natural disasters. Millions of people will be displaced from their homes and homelands and become climate refugees, only to experience, in some cases, a lack of compassion from the people they look to for help.

We can and should do whatever is possible to address humanity's problems at scale in order to lessen human suffering.

The second point is: **Sometimes we are the ones suffering, and when that is the case, we can seek meaning in the suffering**—some kind of purpose that encourages us on, widens our view of the world, and joins us more deeply in the human community. At the very least, we can will ourselves to turn suffering into meaning, then we can direct—if not control—our attitudes toward what we experience.

Finding meaning in our own suffering is the ultimate human triumph. We might question whether there is a limit to the suffering we could endure and still be able to seek meaning and find it, but Viktor Frankl gave humanity the decisive answer to that question through his work. After surviving three years of the horrors of Nazi concentration camps, Frankl wrote *Man's Search For Meaning* —a wise and profound treatise on human dignity and the purpose of suffering.

"If there is a meaning in life at all, then there must be a meaning in suffering. Suffering is an ineradicable part of life, even as fate and death. Without suffering and death human life cannot be complete."

— Viktor E. Frankl, *Man's Search for Meaning*

But again, enduring our own hardships and finding purpose through them is not the same as expecting others to do the same. Where pain is concerned, our efforts to find insights should be directed inward, and our compassion and aid directed outward. Attempting to find meaning in the suffering of others can lead us into strange rationalizations and victim-blaming. So here is another opportunity to embrace both/and thinking: to try, wherever possible, to relieve other people's suffering with urgency while finding meaning and purpose in how we endure and overcome our own.

Navigating ambiguity

Perhaps predictably, over the past year, throughout the pandemic and the big pivot to virtual events, this theme of Strategic Optimism gained resonance with people and teams who wanted to be offered hope—not as platitudes or mere reassurance, but in a useful framework that can apply to their strategic direction. In one of the most serendipitous[39] examples, the Google Geo team (which includes their Maps, Earth, and Street View products as well as AR and other emerging products related to geographic information) brought me on to engage with them about a combination of Tech Humanism, Pixels and Place, and Strategic Optimism, all around the theme of "navigating ambiguity." A great pun and an inspiring topic. Win-win.

Ambiguity and anxiety

As we face our future to make it brighter, we will come face-to-face with one of the sources of human anxiety: ambiguity and the unknown. We have a complex relationship with these dynamics because we're biologically wired to react to what we know or can sense about our environment. Dealing with anything we can't sense fully means we're not operating from our animal instincts, which happen in the parts of our brains that are evolutionarily the oldest and most established. The parts of our brains that are capable of higher reasoning, extended inferences, and extrapolation are newer systems, but they're built right on top of those older systems.

Are you familiar with the Winchester Mystery House? The one where rooms are added on in all sorts of bizarre ways? The human brain is not unlike that house.

You already know what this means in practice: fight or flight. When confronted with stressful situations or hard decisions, our brains default to reacting as if we're staring down a Bengal tiger. And that leaves us, the supposedly evolved human being, trying to make rational decisions while experiencing fear and denial.

Fear as well as anger both have valid places in the discussion about the future. But once we acknowledge them, they're mostly useful when they're galvanizing. If they encourage us to act, they're tools we can use. If they're holding us back from action, we need to work through them.

Fortunately, we can rewire our brains, at least somewhat. We can practice awareness and be mindful about our reactions while cultivating a mindset of agility for dealing with change. It's a discipline, like exercise. And just as regular

---

[39] À propos of nothing, "serendipity" is my favorite word. I mean, seriously, what a great word. Don't get me started on how much I love geeking out about words and language.

exercise challenges our muscles, the goal is to give our brains new strength and flexibility.

Faced with big implications about big tech, for example, we need the clarity to make quick decisions about policy and consumer protections—and we don't want these decisions to be reactionary or lacking in informed insight. The rapidity of the growth in the Change Factors means we will need to make policy decisions before it feels like we have gathered all the facts.

During the COVID-19 pandemic, health organizations and local governments have had to make judgment calls about policies like mask mandates and lockdowns without the certainty of scientific consensus. Public opinion, which typically reacts to the latest headlines and in this case, reacted much too late, only exacerbated the situation. Historians will no doubt study this period of time with interest because it contains such vastly differing approaches, such political contradictions, and such mixed results. But the challenge throughout the pandemic has been: How do you make decisions, how do you lead, when you don't know what you're dealing with?

Business leaders had to decide whether and when to send workers home; whether to reopen stores, restaurants, and offices; and how to keep their employees healthy, informed, and confident that the right decisions were being made.

None of this has been easy. And none of it is really over. The Change Factors we face, from the climate crisis to intelligent automation, are still with us, advancing with or without our conscious involvement. In order to contend with them, we need to shake off complacency and recognize what needs to be recognized. Not all of it is so ambiguous.

Facing your feelings

Change is hard for most people; exponential change of any kind is daunting. The kinds of intersecting exponential changes we now face may be enough to invoke panic responses, and some people may prefer to shut out any further information on a subject they feel powerless to deal with. No doubt, it's easier to binge-watch escapist TV shows than to absorb more news about existential threats to our species.

Fear is a natural response, an animal response, and the fact that we feel it is a good sign. But what should we do with fear? As humans who have evolved the ability to reason, we have an obligation to harness the fear and the opportunity it opens up. Fear is telling us to watch out on one side, but it's also telling us the other side may be safer. We need to look toward the safety, understand it, and reinforce it against that which we fear.

One of the side effects of confronting the fullness of our present situation can be overwhelm; we're bound to feel anxiety, grief, denial. Those reactions are natural, and when we deal with them honestly, they can be useful indicators of what we know needs to happen next.

Living in the cone of uncertainty

How well can you live in an uncertain state, and for how long? Can you *thrive* amid uncertainty? Most people would say no. Dealing with the unknown and the unknowable is what gives some of us the most anxiety.

Entire industries, such as insurance, exist to manage the uncertainty in our world. But how do we manage it for ourselves, in our own lives?

We can never remove uncertainty entirely—after all, none of us actually *knows* the future—but we can learn to make better forecasts and predictions, and we can learn to think probabilistically. You can even teach yourself how to do that by reading books or watching talks online about it.

How can you make decisions when you don't have all the facts?

We have to learn to accept that there are answers we will not have before we have to make decisions.

Perhaps it helps to think about life in general the way you think about weather forecasts: You're looking for directional guidance, not 100 percent accuracy, and even with a meteorology report there's always a high likelihood that something's going to change.

The Hurricane Center also takes care in how it presents the uncertainty in its forecasts. "Uncertainty is the fundamental component of weather prediction," Mayfield said. "No forecast is complete without some description of that uncertainty." Instead of just showing a single track line for a hurricane's predicted path, for instance, their charts prominently feature a cone of uncertainty—"some people call it a cone of chaos," Mayfield said. This shows the range of places where the eye of the hurricane is most likely to make landfall.

—**Nate Silver,** *The Signal and the Noise: Why So Many Predictions Fail—*
But Some Don't [40]

The cone of uncertainty—or cone of chaos—that this excerpt refers to is perhaps an apt metaphor for the chaos in our lives. We know that now and then disaster will make landfall, but we have to be able to enjoy life and get things done anyway.

Thinking about the future in this open-minded and open-ended way can help us to leave room for the inevitable tragedies that collide with our lives now and then, while we continue to focus on moving toward the best futures possible.

[40] Silver, Nate. The Signal and the Noise: Why So Many Predictions Fail--but Some Don't. United States, Penguin Press, 2015. p.138

PART TWO:

Illuminating the Future

*We need a way to think about and talk about the future
that acknowledges risks and harms
while also looking for the brightest possible outcomes.*

Chapter 4:

What is the future?

THROUGHOUT MY YEARS OF ADVISING leaders on future-ready strategy, I've noticed that—consistently—when most people turn their mind's eye toward the future, it is usually in the interest of solving a range of pressing problems that stem from uncertainty, such as:

- Developing forecasts, plans, and roadmaps that anticipate where resources should be invested and which priorities should be made

- Managing variance in timelines, budgets, and hopes

- Coping with anxiety about the unknown

Uncertainty is around us and within us, and it's a valid reason to ask questions about the future. But especially over the years just leading up to 2020 and now since, as we've become more aware of the impact of data on the decisions people make and the impact of everything on the climate emergency and on social justice—the idea that everything is connected has become a driving thesis in my work. This connectedness exists at a cellular level, in the quantum mechanics of our every decision, in ways both too subtle to be perceived and too obvious to be ignored.

I have worked in technology and innovation for twenty-five years, and as time went on and technologies evolved, I believed I had found the central question of my work: How can I—how can we—help humanity prepare for what (by all indications) looks to be an increasingly tech- and data-driven future? But in these last few years, that question has expanded in scope as I've recognized that our collective approach to the Change Factors—climate, politics, misinformation spread, and so on—is similar to how we deal with technology, and just as important as technology in determining how humans can thrive in the future.

After all, since I talk about the future in the context of technology and human experiences, I have sometimes been dubbed a futurist. (In fact, I think it was a podcast interviewer who first described me as an "optimistic futurist" and I immediately loved how true it felt, so I embraced it—years before I ever began writing this book.) But while most futurists traffic in predictions, that's not where I spend my time. I work instead in insight and foresight; my expertise is in human experience strategy, but that just happens to be a flashlight you can shine on a wide array of topics to illuminate useful patterns and determine how they seem to be shaping the future.

Here's a little secret: If we want to, any of us can observe the future being made trend by trend in real-time by watching patterns play out in culture; they tend to predict what comes next, if you learn how to notice them. (You can read more about that in Insights and Foresight: How to Predict the Future and Why.) That's not mysticism or a magical talent; it's a skill that takes practice, and you can learn it too.

It will only help you so much, though, because it is only when we think about the future as the interconnected outcomes that you shape for me and I shape for you, that it *then* becomes something far more profound than a predictive playing field or a practical planning horizon. Only then does it become the roadmap to our collective destiny. And once we see it that way, we owe it to each other to commit to making that future the best it can be.

Okay, but still: what even *is* "the future"?

It's a fair question. For all the talk about the future, it can be a bit of a hard concept to define. After all, it includes the horizon of time from this very next second to millions of years from now.

Most people's thoughts about the future do tend toward specific timeframes: the coming year or so, the coming decade or so, the rest of their lifetimes, and maybe their children's lifetimes. And while many of us have worries about what the future holds in these timeframes, what most people worry *about* tends not to be sci-fi and abstract, but rather rooted in human experience.

As it turns out, when people are asked about what they fear the most, oftentimes they talk about things that are uncertain. They don't tend to be worried about the possibility of water shortage decades from now; they worry about people they love getting sick or dying. They worry about losing their jobs or otherwise encountering financial instability.

Or if you look at the internet searches people conduct that include the phrase *the future*, some of them explore big open-ended questions like "what is the future of jobs?" or "what is the future of technology?"—but almost as often, charmingly, people are asking the internet how they might meet their future wife or husband, boyfriend or girlfriend. For all our sophistication, we're still pretty simple creatures after all.

The challenge for leaders is to connect with these intensely personal narratives in a way that gives meaning to the abstract humanity-level concerns we all face, in a way that relates them to the very human- and individual-level concerns we already have.

"If humans do not make a greater effort to understand the implications of our actions today, we are in danger of jeopardizing our own humanity."

—**Amy Webb,** *The Signals Are Talking*[41]

If we don't deal with climate change head-on, for one very urgent example, we will face conditions that will endanger the health and even the lives of the people we love. If we don't develop integrative approaches for human flourishing beyond jobs that can be automated, many of us will face financial instability.

---

[41] Webb, Amy. The Signals Are Talking: Why Today's Fringe Is Tomorrow's Mainstream. United States, PublicAffairs, 2016. p. 9.

These are the threats, but they're also the opportunities. And I say that not to be glib, but out of a profound respect for the richness of the untapped potential still ahead of us. Our futures will be shaped by how we access that potential.

Why do we think about or care about the future? What does the future mean to us?

Having said all of that, you might still be thinking: But why do we even care about the future tense? Most animals don't appear to think about or have a concept of the future in the abstract. Some seem to be able to sense imminent danger—as a deer catches the scent of a big cat predator, a frog notices a drop in air pressure, or a dog howls in reaction to some other environmental shift we may not sense ourselves. But humans seem to have made a trade-off of animal skills; our survival instincts are duller than those of most wild animals, but we entertain vivid and rich imaginations that can warn us about dangerous scenarios that might occur hours from now, years from now, or decades from now. Or they might not. Nevertheless, we worry.

Worrying is our natural instinct for survival tuned to the future tense. That's why so often our instinct in thinking about the future is to focus on what could go wrong. It's the same core reason why we tend to assume the worst when we hear about new technologies and advances in science, like cloning or genetic editing; we immediately imagine the worst outcomes. Aside from the evolutionary argument, we might contend that that tendency has developed from living as we do in complex and rapidly-advancing societies, and that we react the way we do because we have learned to hold institutions accountable to do better. But do we?

It may indeed be simpler; we may simply be bracing ourselves emotionally to overcome what we fear is inevitable adversity. When tragedy strikes, people sometimes describe it as "unimaginable." But most of us have preimagined many tragedies, voluntarily or not. We know the tragic landscape well. We just haven't mapped the words to the fears or to the possible losses.

In all likelihood, though, we probably haven't mapped the words to the possible *wins* either. We have given outsized fuel to our fears and not enough oxygen to our hopes. An overemphasis on the worst possible outcomes won't offer us a vision of the best possible outcomes, or a map for walking the rocky, compromised path between them with the least damage and the most chance to do better in the future still further ahead.

We can outsmart our instinctive capacities and do better than worry; we have the capacity to plan, to hope, to imagine, and to lead others to come with us.

Is there one future or are there many possible futures?

Now you're catching on.

While we typically talk about the future as a single collective concept, it's often more useful to think about the *many possible futures* that depend on every single action and decision.

> "If we subscribe to the laws of the universe, we must agree from the outset that there is no one, predetermined future, but rather a possibility of many futures, each depending on a variety of factors."
>
> —**Amy Webb,** *The Signals Are Talking*[42]

The idea of imagining multiple futures may seem to add complexity, but in a way this mindset frees us up: Instead of a hopelessly blurry abstract vision that's way too massive to ever anticipate in perfect detail, we can envision scenarios that may or may not come true, some of which we can influence. If we are to pursue the best outcomes and the brightest paths ahead, we'll stand a better chance if we can see how one decision now creates a cascade of future decisions and opportunities—and how our current indecision may limit us down the road.

So we often lose sight of our role in shaping what's ahead. But the trick to building a brighter future—or indeed, in shaping brighter possible futures—is to recognize that none of it is predetermined, and that we actually have a lot of influence, day to day, on what comes next. Our impact on the possible outcomes for ourselves and others may be infinitesimally hard to measure, but in conscious and unconscious ways, we change the future every day.

---

[42] Webb, Amy. The Signals Are Talking: Why Today's Fringe Is Tomorrow's Mainstream. United States, PublicAffairs, 2016. p. 34.

And even when we feel small compared to the magnitude of problems we see in the world around us, we must remember that we are never truly powerless: The history of the world is culture after culture telling story after story of one person or a small group of people speaking up, getting involved, taking a stand, and making the possible futures brighter for the others who come after them.

Chapter 5:

Thinking holistically, acting collectively

IN THE SOCIAL JUSTICE SPACE, there is a commonly-cited notion: "Impact matters more than intent." In other words, your good intentions mean little if you perform them in a way that ignores their outcome and the harms they may inflict upon others. That's because the moment you take an action, it very likely affects other people.

We're all individuals, and also we're not

With decisions at scale, individuality becomes a dot in a pointillist painting. The whole of the picture shapes culture. That's not to say the dot doesn't matter; of course it does on its own scale. That's also not to say that individuality, identity, and personal autonomy are not important constructs; of course they are, not least because out of individual identity comes a consciousness that seeks meaning and everything associated with it: purpose, significance, etc. But one dot's individual "dotness" doesn't override the importance of the rest of the dots. Both individual rights *and* collective human rights matter. We need to plan for the future of the dot and the whole painting simultaneously: at human-scale and humanity-scale.

As I write this, the world is facing a deadly pandemic, and the primary mechanism for containing its spread is for everyone to recognize our role in an interconnected network of disease—contagion that could reach, infect, and even kill us or someone we care about. But even if it only devastates people we don't know personally, that should matter too. It can be hard, though, to care about that which seems removed and disconnected from us.

Perhaps we need better reminders of how connected we truly are. After all, the whole biological world is interconnected. No, that doesn't reach far enough: The entire *universe* is interconnected. Whenever you need to think about yourself in a more cosmically connected way, remember that the carbon, nitrogen, iron, and other elements in our bodies were all part of long-ago dying stars perhaps far beyond our own galaxy. In ways literal enough to metaphorically blow your mind, we are in the universe, and the universe is within us.

We think we are shaped by external forces, but we have more influence on the "external" world than we think. We tend to think of ourselves as small, independent figures, and what difference could our decisions possibly make? This demonstrates that perhaps we need a new way to think about our decisions.

PART THREE:

Get Clear About the Change Factors

*Strategic Optimism starts with looking candidly at our situation
and then determining what is important,
what will be important, and what we would most like to see happen.*

Chapter 6:

Understanding exponential changes and complexity

Things are changing fast.

Most of the change we're used to experiencing and observing happens at a linear rate. We're (usually) born one at a time, and we (usually) die one at a time. That linear progression feels ingrained in our subconscious, and it makes that pattern of growth and decay feel natural to us.

Quite simply, if something grows each day on this scale, over the course of about a week and a half it will look like:

1, 2, 3, 4, 5, 6, 7, 8, 9, 10, and so on.

However, if something is growing at a rate where it, say, doubles each day, in that same week and a half span it would look more like:

1, 2, 4, 8, 16, 32, 64, 128, 256, 512, 1024, and so on.

We notice a striking numerical difference, and the gap between the scales grows more extreme with time. Colloquially we describe this as exponential growth[43]—the kind of growth that seems slow and small for a time and then happens massively all at once. For example, consider how Mike in Hemingway's *The Sun Also Rises* says he went bankrupt "gradually, then suddenly." Perhaps you can relate to the feeling.

We have seen this with the viral outbreak of COVID-19. Each infected person can infect multiple people, and once those people are infected, they in turn can infect multiple others. What adds to the complexity of understanding the coronavirus outbreak phenomenon is the delay between the initial infection and when the symptoms appear and the patient tests positive for the virus. During that asymptomatic period, the infected persons may infect a staggering number of others who will also be days away from appearing on case reports and graphs. As such, we go from seeing what looks like a small number of cases to a mind-blowing rise in cases each day.

We have to think exponentially about our Change Factors too. But the good news is we also have access to exponential resources; emerging technologies bring added capacity and scale like never before. Computational power has been doubling every year or two for decades, as famously recognized by Gordon Moore in 1965 as Moore's Law.[44] Of course, our brains haven't changed that much since the origin of *Homo sapiens*, but that's why it helps to understand our innate Human Superpowers, which can help us thrive amid change.

Still, we are struggling to make sense of this rapid growth.

The climate crisis is happening at a scale that is challenging to comprehend, because it is both so vast—manifesting in ways everywhere around the world—and so small as to seem insignificant in terms of the macro discussion about the

---

[43] I say "colloquially" here because the mathematics of exponential growth are a bit more convoluted, and can sometimes even mean very slow growth. But culturally it refers to the kind of growth that happens when things, say, double in rate or size.

[44] Moore, Gordon E. "Cramming more components onto integrated circuits." April 19, 1965. intel.com. Electronics Magazine.

increase in global average temperature by 1 or 2 degrees Celcius. In reality the difference between 1.5 and 3 degrees includes a litany of devastating impacts, but because the numbers are small, it's hard for an individual to register the likely effects.

But collectively we face several other kinds of exponential change: AI, emerging technologies, and the fallout of geopolitical upheavals, all of which are happening in combination with each of these other things. The COVID-19 pandemic is yet one more form of exponential change that has affected everyone on the planet in some way, and among other outcomes, it is reshaping the workplace.

So it's critical for us to think in an integrative way about building effective workplaces, cities, institutions, businesses, and careers to align with the future that is emerging.

Faster, more complex, more connected, more dystopian?

If you've ever wondered if life seems to be going faster and becoming more complicated, that's not just your imagination; technology has been speeding up the manufacture and production of goods for quite some time, and newer technologies keep accelerating how we communicate, how we consume, and how we experience everything else around us. Meanwhile, the introduction of these technologies has added more complexity to the world and to our lives.

The good news and bad news is that with all this complexity and acceleration, everything also becomes more connected. And exponential connectedness brings scale. Things matter at scale and in aggregate that may not matter as much individually, and it's up to us to learn to recognize these systems and to insist on better from companies, from governments, and from ourselves.

Our new mindset should involve a more holistic, integrative, both/and kind of thinking because we need to be able to talk about what's happening in constructive and destructive ways, and we need to be able to do so on both the human-scale and the humanity-scale. We need to consider both individual, human-level consequences of decisions and broader, more integrated consequences on communities, society at large, and humanity at scale.

In our collective future, it is because of the dramatic nature of the overlapping forces of change that we can find hope. We can see how they intersect and influence one another. We're not *just* dealing with climate change, and we're not *just* managing the COVID-19 pandemic; many other factors are combining, and the conditions they create may certainly create worsened conditions in the short term—but that also means they are poised for a wholesale leveling up if we do the work systemically and holistically.

The pandemic set in motion a series of very difficult circumstances for all of us. Between trying to stay healthy, trying to stay employed, and trying to stay sane amid heavy restrictions on life as we knew it, we have had a lot to deal with. Mental health has been widely reported to be affected. It's wearing people down.

And what I see as the even bigger frustration is how we haven't learned the key lessons from this episode. We haven't learned to listen to science, we haven't learned the importance of committing to modifying our own individual behavior as part of a collective movement of behavior change in the interest of the public good, and we haven't learned well enough how to apply upward pressure on institutions—such as government and corporations—to insist on better protections for people.

We need to learn these lessons for any number of reasons—in part because another novel virus could be around the corner at any time, and because in our globally-mobile society, hopscotching the planet on increasingly affordable international flights and routinely crisscrossing international borders for work and pleasure makes us more vulnerable to pandemics than at any time in history. And in a broader sense, these lessons also apply to how we must manage and mitigate the climate crisis and the changes needed on every level to deal with it.

We want our bright future, and that future should center the value of life and balance—as well as joy, love, harmony, justice, peace, and beauty of all kinds, made possible for all people.

As such, we have to keep multiple truths in our minds at the same time. That's not something we've always demonstrated great skill at, but I believe we can do it.

Chapter 7:

Acknowledge the fullness of the situation

THE BRIGHTEST FUTURES WILL ONLY be possible if we shine the light of truth on our current situations to see them clearly. Our global challenges, including the climate crisis, are high-profile enough to have generated volumes of research, books, articles, and discussion. How do we sort out what is credible and what does not deserve our trust? That's a subject we'll dig into in Chapter 20: A Brighter Future for Truth and Trust.

But when it comes to issues facing your business, your personal life, or the world at large, what we need to know is that ignoring the information out there won't do us any favors.

And true, whether we're dealing with a personal assessment of a current reality, a business predicament, or the whole of our collective global challenges, the whole truth can feel like a lot to process.

But we need to take account of it all: the good stuff, the bad stuff, the I'm-not-sure-what-this-is-yet in-between stuff. Are some jobs being displaced by automation, to take one Change Factor as an example? Yes. Are some jobs being created by automation? Yes. Do the new jobs require different skills from the old jobs? Often. Do the people who've been displaced and who don't have the skills for the new jobs have some other emerging opportunities? It's not clear; let's find out. We'll dig into that discussion further in Chapter 15: Meaningful Work versus Meaningful Jobs.

Recognize the harms

We cannot build the best futures for the most people if we are afraid to face truths about the suffering the current situation may be causing.

We need to challenge ourselves to see—really see—the people who are living amid injustices of various kinds relating to the present state. On a personal level, that may mean owning up to behaviors we are engaging in that hurt and disappoint people, for example. Corporate leaders may need to confront unsustainable business models that rely on exploited labor or downstream impacts of their products or services that disproportionately harm communities of color or people who are already living on society's margins in some way. Too many industries rely on outsourced manufacturing in countries where neither the business leaders nor the majority of consumers can see potential human trafficking and forced labor, and we look away from the human cost in keeping prices down. That was never a good tradeoff; the future demands better.

And collectively, we can only address the injustices of environmental racism, for example, by taking an open-minded assessment of which communities are most impacted by, say, air quality issues from our nearby factories or lack of clean water availability due to our industrial runoff.

These are painful things to take stock of. Denial is an easier path, but leads to distancing ourselves further from the kinds of actions and decisions that would begin to remedy what's not right.

It should be a priority to center those who are most harmed by our actions and inactions—they are de facto stakeholders—and involve them in setting the agenda for change.

Whatever the topic, if there's bad news to know or hard pills to swallow, we need to face them upfront so we don't get discouraged once we're actively trying to solve the problems and running into obstacles we could have foreseen by a more candid assessment.

Chapter 8:

Solving at scale

ONE OF THE CHARACTERISTICS OF topics like the climate crisis, say, or artificial intelligence is how big and overwhelming they tend to feel. The topics are vast, filled with myriad subtopics and related discussions. It feels like you start down one conversational direction and you wind up in another.

Part of the reason they feel so vast and daunting is because many of these topics do interconnect; for example, climate action is inseparable from social justice due to consequences that play out in different ways for different regions where different people live, and both of these topics are inseparable from geopolitics and the rise of authoritarian and fascist regimes that take advantage of people's fear and anxiety about change.

It's also part of the reason why we must acknowledge that Everything Is Connected, as I cover elsewhere, but it's also why we must think about solutions that can address these problems at a level that can at least hope to match their own impact. In other words, we need solutions *at scale*.

In my experience, a pretty good amount of what goes wrong happens as a result of not having thought enough about what could go right—because "going right" for many experiences means achieving scale, and scale is a stress test for how meaningful experiences are and how much thought has gone into their impact.

Smaller, incremental changes are often important stepping stones because they can help us change our behavior and mindset. They can also lay the groundwork for larger change, but when we have solutions that *can* scale, we must prioritize building them out with the infrastructure and resources they'll need to make an impact.

I tend to focus on how tech can amplify what is meaningful and help humanity at scale without adding to harms. This is partly because my own career has grown out of two and a half decades in and around technology, and it is natural for me to look at problems and potential solutions with technology in my back pocket, ready to pull out and use at any time. But even more so, I believe emerging technologies like intelligent automation have the advantage of capacity that could help us in solving human challenges at scale.

The very concept of building "at scale" could be considered problematic and at odds with the human-centric priorities I am trying to champion. But increasingly, with the proliferation of smartphones, wearables, and Internet of Things (IoT) sensors and beacons, and with the rise in algorithms and machine learning to fulfill and optimize human experiences, technology already has inherent scale and reach—the design and building of which deserves our utmost consideration and care.

In addition, many of the world's most pressing problems are themselves at scale: the scale of humanity's existence on the planet. So as more tech-driven experiences are created, it is my aim to imbue those experiences with as much human orientation as possible, which means infusing them with what is meaningful.

Human-Scale versus Humanity-Scale

For all this talk about solving problems "at scale," there are times when it makes more sense to think small and intimate.

Early on during the pandemic, I wrote about and was advising clients about how service providers needed to sort of downshift from solving problems at a more abstract "humanity" level to solving problems on a more tangible "human" scale. The more urgent problems at the bottom of the Maslow hierarchy were suddenly more important.

When in doubt, bring your focus down from humanity-level to human-level. Ask yourself: How can you help *a human* who is struggling with a problem related to your focus area?

We can always look for solutions that are helping individuals and smaller communities and figure out what we can do to enlarge their impact, expand their reach, and enhance their effectiveness.

Figuring out how to solve for that urgency without losing your positioning or value proposition is a great lesson in resilience and adaptability for brands. Going forward, it'll be a good mechanism and fluency for companies to know how their value proposition scales up and down from the more survival-oriented everyday problems to the more abstract ideas that people gravitate to when they're more secure.

Chapter 9:

Choosing words to inspire action

WHAT HAPPENS WHEN A BRIGHT idea isn't communicated well? It dims. Fewer people can see it and understand it, and fewer positive outcomes will result.

This is the "strategy" work of Strategic Optimism. We have to make our view of the future something others can see, can get on board with, will work for, etc.

Language is one of my favorite aspects of strategy. I've been a strategist throughout most of my career, but I was a linguist by education. The way words and the nuances of language shape the way we absorb ideas and adopt them as our own has fascinated me all along. The linguist George Lakoff has done important work on how the language we use reflects our framing, and how we can use framing more intentionally—more strategically—to convey our values and our messaging.

As a controversial but clear example, regardless of what exactly you may believe about abortion, it should be easy for us to agree that one of the most powerful demonstrations of strategic linguistic framing in the past fifty or so years is the notion of anti-abortion advocates staking the claim of being "pro-life." That bit of language frames the debate into a metaphor that by design forces an opponent to choose whether in response they are going to be pro-(something that life *isn't*, like death) or pro-(something that isn't *about life*, like choice).

It's important to think about how language changes relative to changes in culture and society. Think about how the semantic limitations of too literal an interpretation of the term *global warming* meant that it needed to be updated in common usage to *climate change* and then, to convey more urgency, *climate crisis* or *climate emergency*.

When the *Guardian* updated its style guide in 2019, for example, they revised their guidance on using the term *climate change*:

> "**Climate change** is no longer considered to accurately reflect the seriousness of the overall situation; use **climate emergency** or **climate crisis** instead."[45]

So how do we articulate the future we want to create? How do we express our optimistic vision in strategic language? Here are a few guidelines, using the language of climate crisis as an example.

Choose language that is relatable

If we want our strategic plans for a bright future to be effective, the way we talk about it must resonate with other people. We need to draw parallels with common ideas and use terminology that the people we want to connect with will understand.

Choose language that is clear

Although the climate emergency relates to the overall warming of global temperatures on the macro time scale, not all of the immediate symptoms have to do with warmth. Recurring "polar vortex" snowstorms, for example, are practically an invitation for dumb jokes about global cooling. So to avoid

---

[45] The Guardian, "Guardian and Observer style guide." https://www.theguardian.com/guardian-observer-style-guide-c

bogging down the discourse by having to explain the science, we can instead look to language that more succinctly describes not only symptoms we all can recognize but also the sense of urgency we should feel about them.

Choose language that is motivating

Critics often take issue with efforts to change commonly-used terminology, decrying it as "political correctness." But that's missing the point: The bigger motivation should be in pushing ourselves forward. As this guide on dictionary.com points out:

> "The idea of climate change is scary and overwhelming to most people, but knowing the right words to use to describe what's happening and potential ways to solve problems is a powerful tool in not only managing our collective anxiety—our solastalgia—about climate change, but also in starting discussions that could lead to meaningful action.
>
> "As scientists have told us again and again, avoiding these issues won't make them go away, no matter how inconvenient the truth may be. Addressing them in our language is at least one, if small, place to start."
>
> —The Changing Language Of Climate Change, https://www.dictionary.com/e/new-words-surrounding-climate-change/

Understand the Overton window

When it comes to framing ideas strategically, an important concept to be familiar with is that of the Overton window[46], which represents the window of acceptable ideas, politically speaking.

---

[46] https://www.mackinac.org/OvertonWindow

Coined by Joseph P. Overton in the 1990s[47] while he was as an executive at Mackinac Center for Public Policy[48], a conservative think tank in Michigan, the term was meant to signify that an idea's political viability depends mainly on whether it falls within a certain range, rather than on politicians' individual preferences. His visual illustration of the idea was a brochure with a cardboard cutout slider that would show different policies within the "window" when moved around.

Although political and social discourse is more nuanced than a simple slider would suggest, the Overton window is a tremendously useful concept—partly because we have a tendency to think of *perfect* as the enemy of *good*, when by this model we can better understand how *perfect* can help us move *good* forward.

"The smart way to keep people passive and obedient is to strictly limit the spectrum of acceptable opinion, but allow very lively debate within that spectrum—even encourage the more critical and dissident views. That gives people the sense that there's free thinking going on, while all the time the presuppositions of the system are being reinforced by the limits put on the range of the debate."

—**Noam Chomsky**, *The Common Good*[49]

In short, you can talk about any issue however you want. But if you want to rally support, be understood, and move people to action, it helps to consider your language from a framing point of view.

---

[47] https://www.nytimes.com/2019/02/26/us/politics/overton-window-democrats.html

[48] https://www.mackinac.org/bio.aspx?ID=12

[49] p. 43, The Common Good, 1998

PART FOUR:

Commit to the Brightest Future

Strategic Optimism continues with resolving to do the work to bring about the brightest future.

Chapter 10:

Now that we see it, how do we fix it?

NOW THAT WE HAVE ENVISIONED our boldest future, we need to embrace the work of getting there. We have to agree that incremental failure is bound to happen as we try new things, but quitting and abandoning our goals is not an option. Transformation is a journey in itself, and if we believe in the destination, we can find meaning in the ride.

But this is where our brand of optimism itself becomes a superpower: It can drive us, motivate us, inspire us, make us feel more impassioned and more determined. It can connect us to others who are making their own contributions to the process. It can offer us renewable energy to continually recommit to our emerging reality. It can speak to us from the future and beckon us forward. Optimism is not what happens when we get there; it's what powers us to get there.

One of the values encoded in my previous company, [meta]marketer, was that we should "speak truth to power, but confront with compassion." Many of us have the opportunity from time to time to interact with someone who represents a kind of power, but that person rarely has absolute power. Shouting at them, for example, might be cathartic but would yield no change. My experience has been that it is easier to get someone to hear the challenge you are presenting to their power when you appreciate that they are wary about how making the change you are asking for will affect them.

And let's be clear: I'm not talking about tiptoeing around, say, a fascist dictator's feelings; I'm talking about, for example, speaking in front of an audience of middle managers at a large company and presenting a contextual model about human-centered technology that has been made relevant for them, that dovetails with their daily concerns and their workflow.

There's nothing untruthful about that approach; it is simply looking for every toehold to introduce bigger change.

And yes, we need constructive criticism of power structures and status quo that have led us to where we are. Without articulated criticism, we cannot respond with appropriate solutions. All the optimism in the world won't help make people's lives better if they can't get educated, can't get fed, can't get a job, and so on. So we need to have our eyes wide open about the roots of problems, and then fit our proposed solutions to the truth—not fit our truths to the explanations we're comfortable with.

What does the future need us to do?

Given the choices we've already made in the past about the future that is now our present, we are faced with a certain amount of decision debt that we must repay. Out of enlightened self-interest, the best way forward is an emphasis on regeneration—in climate in particular but also across an array of themes. We are depleted but we have the capacity to heal ourselves and the culture we live in.

In some cases companies' climate action commitments are evolving through their own leadership, while in others, such as ExxonMobil and Chevron, the change is coming from shareholders demanding stronger emissions-reduction strategies and targets. In still other cases, the change may be driven by external forces, such as was the case in May 2021 when Shell was ordered by a court in the Netherlands to cut its carbon emissions by 45 percent by 2030 from the levels measured in 2019. [50]

---

[50] (The Economist Espresso, May 27 2021)

But if you have the choice, set your own agenda for change. When you do, you can better align the strategy with your values, with your culture, and with your existing products and plans. It may turn out that you can be *more* aggressive about change once you look within your own organization.

Chapter 11:

The roadmap to a more just future has already been created

FOR SEVERAL YEARS NOW, I have used the United Nations Sustainable Development Goals with my clients as the beginnings of a helpful roadmap for how we can solve many of the human problems we face at scale by identifying the areas of greatest need.

If you are unfamiliar with them, they are a set of seventeen goals to transform our world, often presented in a colorful grid such as the one shown above, and numbered for easy reference:

Goal 1: No Poverty

Goal 2: Zero Hunger

Goal 3: Good Health and Well-being

Goal 4: Quality Education

Goal 5: Gender Equality

Goal 6: Clean Water and Sanitation

Goal 7: Affordable and Clean Energy

Goal 8: Decent Work and Economic Growth

Goal 9: Industry, Innovation and Infrastructure

Goal 10: Reduced Inequalities

Goal 11: Sustainable Cities and Communities

Goal 12: Responsible Consumption and Production

Goal 13: Climate Action

Goal 14: Life Below Water

Goal 15: Life on Land

Goal 16: Peace, Justice and Strong Institutions

Goal 17: Partnerships for the Goals

Some of these ideas will have overlap in their execution, such as Goal 4: Quality Education and Goal 5: Gender Equality. Which makes sense: Not only is each one of these goals worth aspiring to and working toward on its own merit, but taken as a set they reinforce one another and can yield interaction effects well beyond the targets. In fact, some research has examined the synergies and tradeoffs between the goals in order to best understand how to achieve them most effectively, identifying for example that Goal 11: Sustainable Cities and Communities and Goal 13: Climate Action are strongly aligned, as are Goal 1: No Poverty and Goal 4: Quality Education.[51]

The SDGs, as they are commonly known, were developed in September 2015 to be measurably improved by 2030. So the 2020s are the decade of action.

As of this writing, however, we are woefully behind on meeting them.

During a 2021 address to the Opening of the Ministerial Segment of the High-Level Political Forum on Sustainable Development (HLPF), the UN's core platform for review of the 2030 Agenda for Sustainable Development and its seventeen SDGs, Secretary-General António Guterres reported: "Violence against women has risen to shocking levels, with reports doubling and tripling in some places. An added burden of unpaid domestic and care work is squeezing women out of the labor force."

He added: "I continue to believe that we can and must turn this around. We have the knowledge, the science, the technology and the resources to do so. What we need is unity of purpose, effective leadership from all sectors, and urgent, ambitious action."[52]

---

[51] Pradhan, P., Costa, L., Rybski, D., Lucht, W. and Kropp, J.P. (2017), A Systematic Study of Sustainable Development Goal (SDG) Interactions. Earth's Future, 5: 1169-1179. https://doi.org/10.1002/2017EF000632

[52] United Nations Secretary-General, "Secretary-General's remarks to the Opening of the Ministerial Segment of the High-Level Political Forum on Sustainable Development [as delivered]," July 13, 2021. https://www.un.org/sg/en/content/sg/statement/2021-07-13/secretary-generals-remarks-the-opening-of-the-ministerial-segment-of-the-high-level-political-forum-sustainable-development-delivered

To pursue ambitious action, we need to look up out of our local markets and ecosystems and see how we connect to and impact the world. And the exponential capacity and scale of emerging technology—along with all of the other exponential and existential changes we're facing as both opportunities and threats—demand that we shake off the limitations of our inadequate ways from the past of thinking about the future.

In the coming chapters, we will see how cultural change, technology and innovation, and new ways of thinking can help us address the challenges outlined by these seventeen goals at scale, through smart and intentional use of tech tools, through concerted efforts of business and industry, through governmental interventions, through institutional efforts, and through collective action by individuals acting in roles as voters, consumers, neighbors, and citizens.

Chapter 12:

Envision bold ways forward

When you were a child, you probably saw imaginative depictions of the future you might live to see. Maybe they included jet packs and flying cars. Maybe those imaginings featured mind-reading technology, space travel, or any number of other visions creative people throughout the years have offered to us.

Most of those things have yet to come to pass. But, to paraphrase a popular tweet format, "We were promised flying cars!" doesn't register as a worthwhile criticism of the present when we're typing it with our thumbs into supercomputers connected to a global information-sharing network of satellites and suboceanic cables.

We might not always make accurate predictions, but our visions of the future should be daring and grand, even if we fall short.

After all, if we always do the same things, we'll always get the same results. Until we don't. Diminishing returns can always cut into our comfort zone. That's happened to industry after industry over time, and the worst offenders, like the tobacco industry, see the change coming and do everything in their power to ride it out without looking for a newer, more human-aligned solution.

That's not bold, it's not hopeful, and it's not innovative.

We can do better.

We can challenge ourselves to see what isn't yet there, but could be. And we could start to build toward it.

When in doubt, remember:

Work toward the best futures for the most people.

PART FIVE:

The Brightest Futures: Applying Strategic Optimism

Here's how we apply the Strategic Optimism Model to a variety of human subjects.

Chapter 13:

The Opportunity for Human-Centric Tech and Innovation

We have an opportunity for human-centric technology to solve some of these problems at scale.

Indistinguishable from magic: brighter futures for technology

Do you remember the first time technology thrilled you? You may know this quote from Arthur C. Clarke—Clarke's third law: "any sufficiently advanced technology is indistinguishable from magic"? I remember quite clearly when I felt that for the first time: It was in the early nineties, when I first saw the graphical web. In that moment, everything about what I was looking at seemed so magical.

Maybe you're young enough that the visual, graphical web as we know it now came about before you were born, or maybe you were around but weren't paying as much attention to the web or technology at that point. So you might not realize that in the earliest days of the World Wide Web, the browser was just a text browser. The web itself was a remarkable step forward, but Lynx (yes, spelled like the cat) looked very much like any other text-based terminal you've seen:

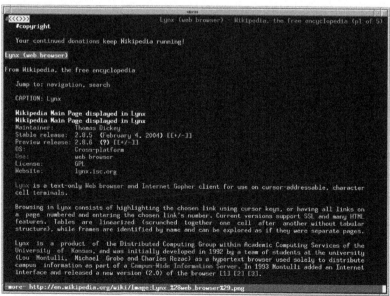

Lynx browser screen capture. Image via Wikipedia[53].

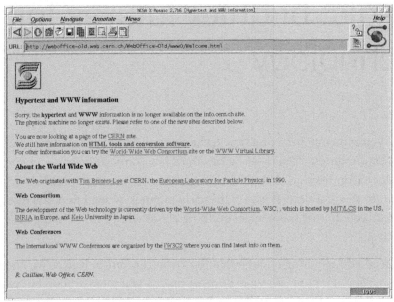

Mosaic browser screen capture. Image via Wikipedia[54].

But then, ah! Once Mosaic came about, you could see embedded *pictures* and you could *format text*. To the contemporary eye the Mosaic rendering of a web page may look ugly and primitive, but need I remind you? Go back and look at the text-based browser! You may appreciate the advances a bit more. There was just so much possibility, and when I first saw Mosaic I remember having tingles on the back of my neck—that feeling when you can just tell something is really special and you think:

This is going to change everything.

And it did! As you know. We're living in a time that has been greatly shaped by everything that came after that—with so much of our lives lived out online or enmeshed with our online experience.

---

[53] The original uploader was Tedickey at English Wikipedia. - Transferred from en.wikipedia to Commons by IngerAlHaosului using CommonsHelper., CC BY-SA 3.0, https://commons.wikimedia.org/w/index.php?curid=8996662

[54] By Programm: National Center for Supercomputing Applications - Screenshot, selbst erstellt, CC0, https://commons.wikimedia.org/w/index.php?curid=75617889

In one sense, the Web as a whole but especially the visual Web allowed us to create layers of knowledge and communication. Rather than flat pages of finite information, ideas could link to other ideas, with visual cues to the contextually-relevant meanings that we could connect and discover in just-in-time learning experiences.

And of course technology has continued to advance and mature—so much so that the set of technologies we commonly refer to now as "emerging," such as robotic automation, the Internet of Things, machine learning, and other artificial intelligence, stands to add tremendous capacity and scale to business operations and fundamentally change human experiences.

In fact, I remember the next time I had that "technology is indistinguishable from magic" feeling: the first time I saw augmented reality. I got those same tingles on the back of my neck and had the same thought: *This is going to change everything!* And—it has not changed everything. But it still can.

Augmented reality, even more so than graphical web browsers, is all about surfacing meaningful information in timely and contextually relevant ways. Think, for example, about using your phone to walk around a foreign city. You can hold it up to a sign in a foreign language to see the message in your own language. Then you can get walking directions that account for needs you specify, such as: "I'd like to pick up a coffee on the way to the museum." So you point your phone in the direction of the museum and receive tips about which way to walk to grab a doppio from the espresso joint favored by locals. Perhaps your phone also points out interesting historical markers as you walk.

All of this is happening on your phone because that's what you, in this scenario, have on you. But all of this could just as easily be happening on your wristwatch or bracelet, or your glasses, or your contact lens. Or even through your headphones: augmented reality audio is a newer field than visual AR, but given how quickly smart speakers and voice interfaces are growing in popular usage (some research predicts a $22 billion market for speech and voice recognition tools by 2026[55]), audio AR hints at a whole array of incredible experiences for accessibility, gaming, entertainment, travel, and well beyond.

Augmented reality should be compelling for retailers and businesses because research has shown that AR in the early stages of customers' buying

---

[55] MarketsandMarkets, "Speech and Voice Recognition Market worth $22.0 billion by 2026" https://www.marketsandmarkets.com/PressReleases/speech-voice-recognition.asp

journeys encourages new kinds of customer creativity through engagement and intrinsic satisfaction[56]. The research frames the role of AR in customers' experiences as "turn[ing] underlying interactions with standardized products and services into creative playgrounds for customers." In other words, the use of AR has the potential to take everyday objects and our surroundings and encourage us to play and interact with them in ways that might inspire us to think about our surroundings differently. Take the IKEA Studio app, for example, which is an evolution of the IKEA Place app I wrote about in my 2016 book, *Pixels and Place*. Expanding from the ability to merely visualize one product in a room at a time, the IKEA Studio app lets customers tinker with combinations of furniture and decorations to create entire room designs.[57]

Of course, home decor isn't the zenith of what can be achieved with this technology. These apps are just vivid illustrations of how AR tools are evolving, and how much immersive activity is becoming possible with them. Imagine how much good AR could do in helping visitors find their way around complex and unfamiliar buildings like hospitals, where they have loved ones undergoing treatment; or helping travelers find their way around new cities; or helping field researchers quickly identify plant or animal species in, say, rainforests where they're studying natural phenomena. Imagine having a food allergy and being able to determine quickly which foods in a foreign supermarket you should steer clear of. Spend another two minutes imagining scenarios where augmented reality can be helpful to humans in the future, and I bet you'll have tingles on the back of your neck too.

---

[56] Alexander Jessen, Tim Hilken, Mathew Chylinski, Dominik Mahr, Jonas Heller, Debbie Isobel Keeling, Ko de Ruyter,
The playground effect: How augmented reality drives creative customer engagement,
Journal of Business Research,
Volume 116,
2020,
Pages 85-98,
ISSN 0148-2963,
https://doi.org/10.1016/j.jbusres.2020.05.002.
(https://www.sciencedirect.com/science/article/pii/S0148296320302952)
[57] WIRED, "IKEA's Revamped AR App Lets You Design Entire Rooms," Jeremy White, April 20, 2021. https://www.wired.com/story/ikea-revamped-ar-app-design-entire-rooms/

Learning how to use AI for good

Historically, when new technologies are introduced, people feel some anxiety about them. There seems to be a tech threshold at which we freak out and wonder what our value is as humans, what tech means to our existence, and so on.

But the observable reality is perhaps best summarized in Amara's Law, as articulated by Roy Amara, a cofounder of the Institute for the Future, in Palo Alto:

> "We tend to overestimate the effect of a technology in the short run and underestimate the effect in the long run."[58]

Certainly there's more than one way to interpret this idea, and the underestimated long-run effects can just as easily be disastrous as beneficial. But our job is to make sure that, where we can, we tip the scales to beneficial. So how do we do that?

In a previous chapter I introduced the United Nations Sustainable Development Goals (see The Roadmap to a More Just Future Has Already Been Created). And awhile back I started collecting headlines and examples of stories I found where AI was being tested or applied to attempt to solve a problem at scale. When I began collecting these AI proofs of concept, I also started mapping these to the SDGs. Some of the proofs of concept I have found and collected are:

- Find areas with poverty (Goal 1: No Poverty)

- Address food scarcity issues (Goal 2: Zero Hunger)

- Detect diseases in crops (Goal 2: Zero Hunger)

---

[58] https://www.pcmag.com/encyclopedia/term/amaras-law

- Reduce herbicide use (Goal 2: Zero Hunger)

- Detect cancer (Goal 3: Good Health and Well-being)

- Find missing children (Goal 3: Good Health and Well-being)

- Help blind people navigate independently (Goal 3: Good Health and Well-being)

- Help people learn new skills (Goal 4: Quality Education)

- Redress gender inequalities in hiring (Goal 5: Gender Equality)

- Maximize clean water availability (Goal 6: Clean Water and Sanitation)

- Optimize solar & wind grids (Goal 7: Affordable and Clean Energy)

- Combat human trafficking (Goal 8: Decent Work and Economic Growth)

- Upgrade infrastructure efficiency (Goal 9: Industry, Innovation and Infrastructure)

- Simplify access to credit (Goal 10: Reduced Inequalities)

- Enhance air quality (Goal 11: Sustainable Cities and Communities)

- Reduce food waste (Goal 12: Responsible Consumption and Production)

- Accelerate carbon capture and sequestration through simulation (Goal 13: Climate Action)

- Forecast extreme weather events for greater adaptation and resilience (Goal 13: Climate Action)

- Clean up the oceans (Goal 14: Life Below Water)

- Manage forests sustainably (Goal 15: Life on Land)

- Spot nuclear weapon sites (Goal 16: Peace, Justice and Strong Institutions)

This list is nothing more than a quick demonstration of the idea, but even at that it's clear there is tremendous potential here.

Even from beyond our planet, there is potential to use technology for good. Satellites can help connect populations living beyond terrestrial infrastructure for phones and internet, and that can be a fundamental step toward mitigating the inequalities and difficulties addressed by several of the SDGs. And with space-based monitors and sensors observing Earth, we can track changes in sea levels, atmospheric measures, and feed data into the kinds of AI opportunities listed above, such as systems to optimize solar energy and food production.[59]

So perhaps here we have the beginnings of an answer to the question of how to use AI and emerging technologies so that they align with the good of humanity, all life, and the planet. How can we innovate (i.e., create what is going to matter) *while* acknowledging the possible harms of data and technology *and while* mitigating those risks as much as possible? The answer is in the pattern of the ideas above: by aligning our incentives with human outcomes and the health of the planet as a whole. And further: by forming diverse teams, by involving stakeholders in affected communities early in the concept and design, and by committing deeply to sustainability and human quality of life beyond mere lip service.

---

[59] World Economic Forum, "Six ways space technologies benefit life on Earth," Global Future Council
    on Space Technologies 2019-2020, September 2020. http://www3.weforum.org/docs/WEF_GFC_Six_ways_space_technologies_2020.pdf

Fairness and ethics in emerging technology

I've always felt a gravitational pull toward fairness. I joke that it's because I'm a youngest child, and my only tool against the mild abuses of my older brother and sister was to protest that their actions weren't fair.

When I was somewhere around eleven years old, as part of a youth group, I signed up to give a talk on "Fighting Fair." (It was the first public speaking I ever did. Little did I know that's how I would make my living decades later.) I have no idea what made me think I really knew anything about fighting fair, but I did a bunch of research and prep at the public library, and I know I delivered it with conviction.

But as it turned out, fairness would also be a concept I'd return to throughout my later life and career in technology. It's a critical aspect of ethical AI and responsible tech. And it's worth considering what we mean when we talk about it in that context.

Fairness in AI is about making sure the AI is designed to be as equitable or as non-harmful as possible—that the underlying data set is comprehensive and not limited by bias, that the logic encoded into the algorithm doesn't discriminate, and that the outcomes and experience are equitable.

In one episode of the *Tech Humanist Show*, my guest was Dr. Rumman Chowdhury. She talked about responsible AI and some of the challenges of creating guidelines and tools for topics such as fairness and bias mitigation that people can use in practice—especially when they're starting from academic research.

If AI isn't designed to be intentionally as fair as possible, there will be algorithmically enhanced discrepancies in the advantages and disadvantages people have.

It is important to note, as well, that emerging technologies like AI and blockchain come with significant costs. Societal risks and harms, job displacement, and ecological consequences come with the computing power required to run these models.

Take for example the use of blockchain for humanitarian aid, which is surrounded by controversy and known for presenting significant challenges. An estimated 30 percent of foreign aid does not reach the intended recipients.[60] So in May 2017, the UN World Food Programme (WFP) launched a project in the Azraq Refugee Camp in Jordan[61] to use blockchain technology to connect refugees with funds they could spend in the camp's supermarket. The program was hailed as efficient, in that it helped reduce bank costs and transaction fees by 98 percent. The security of the disbursements were ensured through virtual accounts and authorization codes, but also through iris scanning. While biometrics do help easily and efficiently establish identity, prevent fraud, and potentially improve the dignity of the process of receiving aid as a refugee, privacy experts have significant questions about the use of this tech—in particular, how it might enable discrimination and exploitation.

Refugees often have very little agency when it comes to how their cases are processed, and that goes for how their personal data is collected too. As Alexandria Polk writes in *Foreign Policy*, "As more humanitarian aid agencies adopt biometric technology, a 'dictatorship of no alternatives,' a phrase coined by Shoshana Zuboff in her 2018 book, The Age of Surveillance Capitalism, is emerging."[62]

Given these challenges, it is clear we need to approach the opportunities of emerging technology with a clear sense of the risks and harms (which is step one of Strategic Optimism!); yet where possible, when we can center human experience, we may yet be able to leverage the scale at which machine learning and other tools can operate and detect patterns that could offer meaningful solutions to human problems, and help us improve the quality of life for millions of people. It is imperative that we try.

---

[60] Migration Data Portal, "How Blockchain can benefit migration programmes and migrants," Solon Ardittis, February 22, 2018. https://migrationdataportal.org/blog/how-blockchain-can-benefit-migration-programmes-and-migrants

[61] Huffington Post, "How Blockchain Technology Is Helping Syrian Refugees," Siobhan Kenna, November 28, 2017. https://www.huffingtonpost.com.au/2017/11/05/how-blockchain-technology-is-helping-syrian-refugees_a_23267543/

[62] Foreign Policy, "Big Brother Turns Its Eye on Refugees," Alexandria Polk, September 2, 2020. https://foreignpolicy.com/2020/09/02/big-brother-turns-its-eye-on-refugees/

We owe it to ourselves to develop the best technologies possible to solve human problems at scale. But we must also take care that in doing so, we don't create a whole new set of problems even more challenging to overcome than the first.

"Humans in the loop" and the "moral crumple zone"

One consideration in how machine learning can be ethical and accountable that comes with its own set of pros and cons is known as "human in the loop." The general idea stipulates that machines can be trained to look for learnable patterns, and then a human should be involved in reviewing either the decisions the machine recommends, or the edge cases or exceptions it encounters. Think of it as human-augmented machine intelligence.

By the way, the term "human in the loop" is also sometimes referenced in a snide way to describe situations where a human may be doing work behind the scenes that is being passed off as AI, such as when a reporter found in 2019 that 25 percent of calls made by Google's Duplex service, which is supposed to be AI-based, were actually being made by humans[63]. I like to refer to this as the "Moviefone Kramer" scenario, as I explained in *Tech Humanist*:

> "In developing chat-driven interactive systems, there is sometimes a transitional stage where interactions are scripted but humans drive the 'back end' of the interactions. This always reminds me of Moviefone Kramer: the episode of *Seinfeld* where Kramer gets a new phone number and it's only one digit off from Moviefone, the pre-internet era automated phone service that you could call to determine movie showtimes. When George calls Kramer thinking he's called Moviefone and Kramer can't decipher George's touchtone entries, he amends the instructions: 'Why don't you just tell me what movie you'd like to see?'

---

[63] https://www.nytimes.com/2019/05/22/technology/personaltech/ai-google-duplex.html

"This is the sort of inverse uncanny valley of automated interaction: where a human interacts with a system expecting a machine and gets a human instead. So there's not always a very clear-cut distinction between when you're interacting with a human and when an automated process has intervened."[64]

Kramer's antics aside, the "human in the loop" approach can be used to ensure sound results in decision review, data labeling, and other parts of the process where machines are being used for gains in speed and efficiency, such as chatbots and recommenders. Keeping humans in the review loop is supposed to ensure that AI-based outcomes don't stray too far from what was intended by their design and deployment. Human reviewers may even be able to spot and reduce biases that have entered the process (often through whatever data was used to train the model and the subtle or not-so-subtle ways that data may have been skewed), thus preventing those biases from becoming amplified through unsupervised machine learning.

One of the classic examples where machine learning could have tripped us up without careful consideration of what was actually being learned was on its way to becoming a story about how superior AI was at radiology. A project at Google had looked at chest X-rays and trained an algorithm on recognizing anomalies. But upon closer review, rather than detecting the chest problems themselves, the machine learning program was picking up the pattern of pen marks that human radiologists had left on the images.[65]

All that said, though, the burden for the gray areas around automated decision-making, such as those made by autonomous vehicles in near-collisions, is often borne by humans in what has become known as the "moral crumple zone." The phrase was first introduced by Madeleine Clare Elish in 2019 in a paper about human-robot interaction, which explored the design failures of automated systems. In examples that include the partial nuclear meltdown at Three Mile Island nuclear reactor in Pennsylvania in March 1979 and the crash of Air France Flight 447 in 2009, both of which were cases in which the prevailing narrative was that human error was to blame, the research also

[64] O'Neill, Kate. Tech Humanist: How You Can Make Technology Better for Business and Better for Humans. United States, 2018. p. 165.

[65] https://www.statnews.com/2020/09/15/bias-ai-health-care/

explores how complicated system alerts and dependencies made human responses more challenging. Changes in system designs could potentially have made the actions taken by humans more effective or at least less disastrous.[66]

On yet other hand, there have been some "human-unsupervised" successes with using AI to monitor the machine learning done by other AI models. Mastercard, for example, has been using AI to test the algorithmic models that detect fraud.[67] Training one kind of machine intelligence to monitor other kinds of machine intelligence does sound efficient, and it could certainly be part of the solutions at scale that we seek to address our Change Factors. But the big question remains: When and how much should humans be involved as AI advances?

We do not have one simple, clear-cut answer for that. There has, however, been increasing consensus suggesting that humans and machines working together are likely to outperform either working alone, so it behooves us to figure it out. Which is why the field of AI ethics is increasingly vital. We need the scale of solutions that machine learning can provide, and we need experts to weigh in on how to make sure we are scaling the right kinds of solutions.

Algorithmic bias

When Dr. Safiya Noble recognized that searches on Google for "Black girls" yielded mostly pornographic results, that theme became the central topic of her book *Algorithms of Oppression: How Search Engines Reinforce Racism*. It's still one of the most respected books on the subject.

Unfortunately, we have many examples to draw from on this subject to make sure we understand the problem. But one particularly troubling example was when an algorithm used to determine access to healthcare was found to favor white patients who were healthy over Black patients who were less healthy. A 2019 study from UC Berkeley and Chicago Booth found that if the

---

[66] Engaging Science, Technology, and Society, "Moral Crumple Zones: Cautionary Tales in Human-Robot Interaction,"
Madeleine Clare Elish. 2019.
https://estsjournal.org/index.php/ests/article/view/260
[67] Raconteur, "What if machines could teach themselves?", Davey Winder, May 17, 2019.
https://www.raconteur.net/technology/artificial-intelligence/machine-learning-themselves/

bias in the algorithm were corrected, it would admit twice the number of Black patients as before.

Ziad Obermeyer, acting associate professor of health policy and management at UC Berkeley and lead author of the paper, said, "The algorithms encode racial bias by using health care costs to determine patient 'risk,' or who was mostly likely to benefit from care management programs. Because of the structural inequalities in our health care system, blacks at a given level of health end up generating lower costs than whites. As a result, black patients were much sicker at a given level of the algorithm's predicted risk."[68]

If that doesn't make you want to fix the future so that it's brighter for everyone, look at the "filter bubble" that gets created partly by what Google, Facebook, Twitter, etc. want us to see, and partly by our media choices. Look at bias in hiring algorithms: Amazon had an automated recruiting tool that penalized résumés with the word *women*. Humans don't make hiring decisions without bias, so we can do better, but with machines we're handing over the keys. Look at predictive policing and law enforcement algorithms: As a 2019 *Guardian* article puts it, "One officer told the researchers that 'young black men are more likely to be stop and searched than young white men, and that's purely down to human bias. That human bias is then introduced into the data sets, and bias is then generated in the outcomes of the application of those data sets.'"[69] Machines are what we encode of ourselves, yet rather than encoding the best of ourselves, too often we are carelessly building automated echo chambers and indulging in self-fulfilling prophecies.

With data and algorithmic optimization, we go forward by fully acknowledging that algorithmic experiences can go very, very wrong—and that in very real ways, our own lives are connected to those outcomes. Having made those acknowledgements, we must then decide to address them, to unpack them, to improve them. Where we collect data for opportunity, we must use it to create more meaningful experiences and better outcomes. It is up to us to shape the future in the way our hopes are asking us to work for.

---

[68] https://www.eurekalert.org/pub_releases/2019-10/uoc--whc102319.php

[69] https://www.theguardian.com/uk-news/2019/sep/16/predictive-policing-poses-discrimination-risk-thinktank-warns, Jamie Grierson, The Guardian, Sep 16, 2019

Build algorithms and automated experiences with human values

As I wrote in *Tech Humanist* and have said many times before and since: Machines are what we encode of ourselves. And that includes our values and our biases. So we need to encode them with all the human values we can. The decision logic we encode into algorithms will become the backbone of machine learning and artificial intelligence tomorrow.

So when I say "encode them with all the human values we can" I mean: encode machines with the *best* version of ourselves—our most enlightened, egalitarian, equitable selves with our most evolved understandings of the world.

And that means we need to look for ways to **automate the meaningful too**. In other words, with every opportunity we have to build a data-informed and tech-driven workflow, we should ask ourselves: "What is *relevant* to consider here? What is *significant* to the person who will be interacting with this process? What is the *context* in which they are encountering this experience?" All of these questions draw from a framework of meaning.

Applying Strategic Optimism...with and without technology

The scenarios we have explored are not limited to technology but rather are informed by human experience and what factors most shape it—which in some cases involves discussions of technology and in other cases not. Moreover, since I want this to be a guide to innovation and future planning that works beyond today's set of technologies, instead of developing each theme around a technology, I have anchored them in the human experience.

My firm KO Insights remains committed to improving human experiences, and within my work I'll continue to dig deeper into how technology can benefit humanity, both by creating more meaningful experiences and by solving human problems at scale. That commitment will offer further opportunities to examine the potential in technologies like augmented reality, artificial intelligence, and others for their impact on human experiences, and to explore what can go right and what can go wrong along the way.

So while you may have noticed that this isn't a tech book, per se, and the Change Factors we're discussing go beyond those introduced by technology, there are important human-scale aspects to solving human problems, and we would be unwise to overlook the power and potential of the tools in our back pockets. We just have to be very clear from the beginning about how to manage the harms technology solutions at scale can do.

For example, in some of the sections that follow we'll examine the changing dynamics around trust and truth, and where we look for facts and reassurance. We'll look at the changing discourse on privacy, and what that means for our future. We'll examine our responsibilities on an individual versus societal versus institutional level.

As I've said repeatedly, my underlying focus is on how to rally our considerable resources as humans to create the best futures for the most people. I centered that theme in *Tech Humanist*, and that emphasis continues in my research, my writing, my speaking, and throughout my strategic advisory and consulting practice. Whatever it takes to make that happen, let's make that happen.

Machines and meaning

Because everything is connected, the decisions we make about using data and optimizing experiences by algorithms are going to shape outcomes in ways that are all connected. So when we talk about making meaningful human experiences, we also need to remember that meaningful experiences need to be inclusive—that we need diverse perspectives to make inclusive human experiences, or else they won't be meaningful for some of the population.

Consider this famous Bill Gates quote about automation: "The first rule of any technology used in a business is that automation applied to an efficient operation will magnify the efficiency. The second is that automation applied to an inefficient operation will magnify the inefficiency." I think you can talk about this principle in a couple of different ways. You could point out that automation applied to meaning will magnify the meaning, whereas applied to absurdity it will magnify that absurdity. You could also point out that automation applied to a fair society is likely to magnify the fairness, while automation applied to an unjust society will magnify the injustice.

This is why we need to acknowledge that *humans cannot let machines determine meaning.* We have to be very mindful and very present in how we encode what is ethical and what is meaningful to us into the algorithms we define and the automation we create. Every experience we build that is increasingly automated needs to be imbued with our best selves—fully mindful of the outcomes we're trying to create and what we're trying to amplify in society.

Then how do we go about creating more meaningful human experiences? Well, to start, we need to design more integrated human experiences in order to create more meaningful human experiences.

Focusing on what matters: Tech Humanism, not techno-solutionism

There are two dueling tendencies we should avoid: seeing technology as the default answer for every problem, and seeing technology itself as the problem. Both of these ways of thinking about technology are too reductive to be useful.

Technology need not be our default answer, and it is probably not the right way to solve all of humanity's problems. I want to be clear that this is not what I am proposing here.

But neither is technology generating all of the problems we face—even though, yes, human experiences will increasingly be shaped by algorithms, scaled by automation, and amplified through machine learning. The problems with technology are rarely about technology; instead they tend to reveal the decisions of the humans who built everything and set the rules.

Tech will not ruin us *or* save us; our adaptability will save us. And innovation is just another word for adaptability. Innovation doesn't have to be tech as we often think of it; it's not necessarily about a mobile app, an AI system, or robots. Innovation could be understanding that a simple piece of cloth over our mouth and nose can help prevent the spread of an airborne virus. Innovation can be about recognizing a need that may only just now be emerging, then changing what needs to be changed to prepare for it.

Tech is not neutral, as my friend Kim Crayton often reminds us in her anti-racism work.[70] The assumptions codified into algorithms or baked into the data sets that are collected to train machine learning models can do real-world harm.

The opportunity for the brightest future, though, is to use technology's capacity for good: efficiency and scale, while recognizing and managing for the harms that can be done when the wrong decisions are made.

The truth is, technology has tremendous power to amplify and extend our decisions, our values, and our work, and if we use it responsibly and well, we stand to benefit enormously. The biggest problems of the present and the future, especially climate change, can be addressed in countless ways by technological innovations.

---

[70] https://hashtagcauseascene.com/guiding-principles/

Given better input, current technologies offer tremendous opportunities to facilitate solving human problems at scale more efficiently than ever, while also offering better human connectedness. This is not techno-solutionism; rather than leading with technology as our salvation, and without placing too much trust in big tech companies or big tech platforms, we can and must look to the sheer *capacity* of technology as a strategic asset in solving human problems—and humanity's problems—at scale. But to keep our results focused on better human outcomes, our approach must begin with and remain grounded in humanity and human values, understanding what humanity is, what it means to be human. Then we must use technology to amplify those characteristics. It must be global digital transformation that keeps humans at the center—with an emphasis on meaningful human experiences, guided by strategic purpose.

Chapter 14:

A Brighter Future for Our Climate

Acknowledge the climate reality

By almost any reckoning, the climate emergency is the most urgent and existential challenge facing humanity for the foreseeable future. All of the other topics we need to cover on our way to creating a brighter future mean nothing if we don't arrest and reverse carbon emissions, reduce global average temperatures, and begin the work of rebuilding sustainable models for all of our living and working on this planet.

By late 2020, methane deposits in the Arctic were starting to be released by melting, which has climate scientists deeply worried. The warming effect of methane on the environment is eighty times stronger than carbon over twenty years.[71] At the same time, the Arctic Sea had also not begun to freeze at the latest date on record[72]. These and other reports from the Arctic region have experts adjusting their predictions about warming trends, and the follow-on effects from those trends add to the cycle of all the other observable phenomena wrapped up in climate change.

Meanwhile, the Amazon rainforest has been devastated by burning. The plastic-filled oceans are warming. Coral reefs are dying.

Perhaps the most psychologically and sociologically challenging aspect of this massive and thorny mega-problem is that even as we begin to tackle these issues one by one, even as we make concerted efforts toward improving them, we will continue to see worsening effects. As David Wallace-Wells writes in *The Uninhabitable Earth*:

---

[71] The Guardian, "Arctic methane deposits 'starting to release', scientists say," Jonathan Watts, October 27, 2020. https://www.theguardian.com/science/2020/oct/27/sleeping-giant-arctic-methane-deposits-starting-to-release-scientists-find

[72] The Guardian, "Alarm as Arctic sea ice not yet freezing at latest date on record," Jonathan Watts, October 22, 2020. https://www.theguardian.com/world/2020/oct/22/alarm-as-arctic-sea-ice-not-yet-freezing-at-latest-date-on-record

"Some amount of further warming is already baked in, thanks to the protracted processes by which the planet adapts to greenhouse gas."

Climate deterioration will be deeply discouraging, and its effects could even lead many of us to despair and to give up.

At this point you may be thinking, *Hey, wait. I thought this was supposed to be an optimistic book.*

It is. Not only do I have hope, but many of the climate experts I have read and spoken with are hopeful as well. But the first step in Strategic Optimism is acknowledging the full and unvarnished reality, and the hard truth about the climate crisis is that the deeper you look at it, the more you read up, the worse it already looks. Which just means our optimistic strategy in response has to be that much more ambitious, that much more collaborative, and that much more comprehensive.

Following the previous passage in *The Uninhabitable Earth*, David Wallace-Wells continues by saying:

"But all of those paths projected from the present…to two degrees, to three, to four or even five—will be carved overwhelmingly by what we choose to do now."

The message is: It's up to us. We're empowered to set the course for the future. What we need now are bold visions and determined action.

Zero emissions are no longer enough. We need governments and companies and every entity possible to commit to net negative emissions. Cities need ambitious plans for incentivizing buildings that sequester carbon. Companies need logistics overhauls to ensure their supply chains are as compliant as possible, and then some.

Choices at the individual level aren't likely to have the drastic climate-related impacts we need without industrial and institutional change, but as a side note, there *is* interesting psychology wrapped up in how making sustainable choices on an individual level keeps us grounded in the mindset of what needs to change. Given the relatively strong position of trust that companies enjoy, this seems like an excellent opportunity for brands to take on aligned actions that can help move us forward, as we'll discuss in Chapter 20: A Brighter Future for Truth and Trust.

In any case, across all areas of global warming and the climate crisis, we must actively work to make *reversals* on the damage where reversals are possible.

> "We know we can't avoid the cataclysmic impacts of global warming by only focusing on achieving zero net carbon emissions; we must also rapidly re-sequester carbon."
>
> — **from Tom Steyer's foreword to Paul Hawken's** *Drawdown*[73]

What about planting trees? Yes, trees are an incredibly important part of a carbon sink approach, and we definitely need to plant more of them—but there's a catch to how we say we're going to do it. The promise of tree-planting has been such an easy add-on for companies' marketing campaigns to make over the years that there's a backlog of trees to be planted and not enough tree seedlings to keep up with the promises[74]. It's not uncommon for companies to make the commitment to their customers to plant trees first, only for them to struggle to find partners to plant the promised trees. As Dorothea Baur, a leading European ESG (environmental, social, and governance) expert, wryly observed when she was my guest on the *Tech Humanist Show*: "I'm waiting for the day when I look out of my window in the middle of the city and they start planting trees. The whole planet must be covered with trees."[75] So it's going to take more than lip service about tree-planting; we have to actually expand our infrastructural capability to grow and plant them, commit land to that use, and compensate for trees lost in wildfires and other natural disasters.

Speaking of trees, we have an issue with forests too.

---

[73] Steyer, Tom. Foreword. Drawdown: The Most Comprehensive Plan Ever Proposed to Reverse Global Warming. Hawken, Paul. United States, Penguin Publishing Group, 2017. p. viii.

[74] National Geographic, "Planting trees helps fight climate change—but we need billions more seedlings," Kyla Mandel, March 2, 2021. https://www.nationalgeographic.com/environment/article/planting-trees-helps-fight-climate-change-but-we-need-billions-more-seedlings

[75] The Tech Humanist Show, Episode 7, September 4, 2020. https://www.thetechhumanist.com/2020/09/04/the-tech-humanist-show-episode-7-dorothea-baur/

Some countries, including the US, have been reporting their progress by including the "carbon sinks" that large forests provide, while other countries without those natural resources don't have that advantage on paper. This, according to experts, isn't factually wrong, but it obscures the work that's needed to be done, especially by countries that do have high carbon emissions like the US, in order to curb some of the damage.[76]

Making a difference in the climate crisis is the prime example of where collective action is necessary. And one of the ways in which we need to begin to collaborate better is simply to agree on the terms we're using and how we're measuring our progress.

All of this is part of embracing the mindset that says this *can* change. This can improve. We need a can-do mindset, but we also need clarity and collaboration.

> "To protect what we love from danger is a natural human instinct that, when we feel a lack of agency, can easily transform into anger. Anger that sinks into despair is powerless to make change. Anger that evolves into conviction is unstoppable."

> —**Christiana Figueres and Tom Rivett-Carnac**[77], *The Future We Choose: Surviving the Climate Crisis* [78]

And we can't pit the environment against the economy. That model is false and artificial, and it ignores the reality that the environment surrounds the "economy" and shapes it in many direct and indirect ways. (In any case, The Economy Is People, as we'll soon discuss.) In monetary terms, the world's seven most industrialized countries will lose a combined nearly $5 trillion in GDP over

---

[76] The Washington Post, "The giant accounting problem that could hamper the world's push to cut emissions," Chris Mooney and Brady Dennis, April 26, 2021. https://www.washingtonpost.com/climate-environment/2021/04/26/greenhouse-accounting-problem/

[77] Figueres, Christiana, and Rivett-Carnac, Tom. The Future We Choose: The Stubborn Optimist's Guide to the Climate Crisis. United States, Knopf Doubleday Publishing Group, 2021. p. XV

[78] Figueres, Christiana, and Rivett-Carnac, Tom. The Future We Choose: The Stubborn Optimist's Guide to the Climate Crisis. United States, Knopf Doubleday Publishing Group, 2021. p. XV

the next several decades if global temperatures rise by 2.6 degrees Celsius—which is a likely projection according to current government pledges and policies.[79]

We need to recognize the human terms, too, and call out the truths in the climate effort. There *will* be a substantial increase in refugees, meaning policymakers in every country need to catch up with this reality and develop humane, effective processes for asylum and pathways for residency and citizenship.

> "If nothing else, the human tragedies of 2020 have shown us that our lives and livelihoods are entirely dependent on respecting nature. Moving beyond injustice, restoring nature, eliminating racism, and solving the climate crisis can only be achieved if we recognize that they are all fundamentally the same challenge of how humans live well together on this Earth."
>
> —**Christiana Figueres and Tom Rivett-Carnac**[80], *The Future We Choose: Surviving the Climate Crisis* [81]

The need for universal access to healthcare will rise sharply as people—many of whom will be living in poverty—increasingly suffer the health consequences of air and water pollution, heat stress, and diseases transmitted by insects and animals. Care work will be vital in the economy that will emerge, from education and child care to paid family leave.

---

[79] https://www.theguardian.com/environment/2021/jun/07/climate-crisis-to-shrink-g7-economies-twice-as-much-as-COVID-19-says-research

[80] Figueres, Christiana, and Rivett-Carnac, Tom. The Future We Choose: The Stubborn Optimist's Guide to the Climate Crisis. United States, Knopf Doubleday Publishing Group, 2021. p. XVI

[81] Figueres, Christiana, and Rivett-Carnac, Tom. The Future We Choose: The Stubborn Optimist's Guide to the Climate Crisis. United States, Knopf Doubleday Publishing Group, 2021. p. XVI

With climate, everything matters

The ecologist and philosopher Timothy Morton describes global warming and the climate emergency as a whole as a "hyperobject"—an object or concept so vast and complicated that it seems to even defy being an object or thing in the first place. Something with such broad temporal and spatial dimensions and implications is almost ludicrous to think about or talk about. (Ironically, that seems to be more or less a requirement for anything being discussed in this book.) But many of these enormous issues intersect, most pressingly the climate crisis and the many disasters facing humanity and all life on earth if we don't act ambitiously to manage and reverse its effects.

If we put the climate crisis to the "what matters and what is going to matter?" model, it's absurdly broad: It all matters. For the sake of human and other life on this planet, we need concerted, collective action on such a dizzying array of areas that it seems to make the questions irrelevant.

But we only need to step back from trying to sum up the whole problem at once—or, as they say, boil the ocean (if you'll pardon the unfortunate expression)—in order to understand that for different people and organizations there are different priorities.

On a individual level, we have a responsibility to ourselves and to each other to review our consumption patterns, rein in our carbon footprint, and try to amend our habits so they are in line with what is sustainable. Not only do these actions matter in the aggregate, but also they help remind us daily of the brighter future we are trying to create.

For businesses, the responsibility may include strategic adjustments to the supply chain or to materials used in packaging or delivery. Companies might invest in improvements to transportation for employees and customers, perhaps offering public transit incentives to employees, or even investing in a partnership with their municipality to provide electric vehicle charging stations at facilities like offices or storefronts.

Cities have tremendous opportunities to emerge as leaders in this space. Ordinances to protect air and water quality, and measures to offer better transit (such as EV chargers, buses, and trains) and micro-transit options (such as bikes and scooters) are all on the table for cities, and the funding sources range from public-private partnerships to specialized zoning to tax programs to federal and foundation grant money.

Investors can make their voices heard, too, and let companies know climate action is a genuine priority. That's been happening, such as when, as briefly mentioned earlier, on the same day in May 2021, the shareholders of both ExxonMobil and Chevron sent strong messages about getting serious with respect to climate responsibility, while in Europe, shareholder votes and a Dutch court ordered Royal Dutch Shell to cut its emissions faster than they'd already been planning. It was billed by many media outlets as a "bad day for oil," and while it might indeed have felt that way to the leaders of these particular companies as well as those who are more comfortable with their financial stakes in the status quo, what that "bad day" characterization overlooks is how often executive leaders are inclined toward making climate-friendly decisions but fear pushback from their boards or investors. The "safer" decisions they make instead, in terms of their company's politics, aren't always in alignment with what would benefit the rest of us. Activist investors may seem unwelcome, but when they're making priorities known on behalf of humanity, they're ultimately doing us all a service—including the company's leadership.

Incidentally, Shell also had a minor public relations awakening back in November 2020, when the company tweeted a poll asking: "What are you willing to change to help reduce carbon emissions?" The tweet prompted many high-profile figures like Greta Thunberg and US congresswoman Alexandria Ocasio-Cortez to call out the hypocrisy of a company profiting off of fossil fuels asking the public for personal change.[82]

As I've written here, a both/and mindset about this issue is best for us: We do need to embrace our own individual responsibilities, but a major part of doing so is by holding companies and entities with more direct impact on the climate to account for making infrastructural and operational change that can give individuals more freedom to make responsible choices. In other words, for example, an oil company that commits to converting its operations to renewable

---

[82] https://www.theguardian.com/business/2020/nov/03/shells-climate-poll-on-twitter-backfires-spectacularly

energy sources and the infrastructure to support them would be making a substantial impact by offering people the convenience and resources they need.

Of course, nothing is quite that simple, but the work of closing the gap is where the effort needs to go.

Innovating climate solutions with tech and data

Where technology and data-led platforms can help, we need all hands on deck.

As we think about alternatives to fossil fuels, we can look at bike programs and multimodal transit options.

The Citi Bike app in New York City now shows transit information alongside bike rental and docking updates. It's an acknowledgement that for many trips, biking isn't enough, or isn't convenient enough—after all, no one wants to arrive to an appointment sweaty, but in combination with buses or trains, biking can simplify and speed a commute as part of a sustainable lifestyle. The app's features acknowledge the fullness of the situation (step 1), focus on what matters and what is going to matter (steps 2 and 3), and demonstrate an empathetic understanding of what needs to change (step 6)—all vivid proofs of how Strategic Optimism can work in practice.

In another mobility- and transit-related example, the city of Austin's recognition of "the clear synergies between bikeshare and public transit" has been praised as a model for other cities as they attempt to revolutionize mobility options in city spaces. *Bloomberg* reports:

"Not long after the bikeshare service Austin BCycle launched in 2013, local leaders in the Texas capital began to wonder if it might make more sense to give Capital Metro, the regional transit agency, a more active role shaping its future. 'We're a mobility provider,' says Chad Ballentine, Capital Metro's vice president for demand response and innovative mobility. 'It was a natural extension for us.'

"Last fall, as the coronavirus pandemic continued to depress transit ridership, Capital Metro assumed the lion's share of bikeshare planning and oversight, rebranding the system MetroBike. Today a resident or visitor can buy a combined Capital Metro ticket and bikeshare pass with a single click. Looking to the future, Ballentine says the agency will incorporate MetroBike docks into new routes, such as planned MetroRapid bus lines. He also sees bikeshare as a way for the agency to serve people if demand is too light to justify fixed-route bus service."[83]

This idea of city transit agencies moving from seeing themselves as managers of assets (buses, trains) to managers of mobility is somewhat new, but the notion of transit agencies managing bikeshare and multimodal transit options is considered a necessary move, since, due to experience, those agencies are better equipped to facilitate and support a linkage between bikeshare and transit. Also, if transit agencies invest more of their resources, bikeshare experiences could be expanded in real ways.

Another example is Phoenix, Arizona—a city that experiences what's known as the "heat island effect"[84] year round. The heat island effect describes how the densely-populated, central parts of a city with lots of concrete and asphalt will have higher temperatures compared to the less populous areas. Phoenix, of course, is far from alone in struggling with unsustainable characteristics that were at one time designed into place; the majority of US cities are built much the same way, engaging in overconsumption, a disposable mentality, and unmitigated urban sprawl. With studies projecting that US cities could be up to 10 degrees Fahrenheit warmer[85] in the afternoon and 14 degrees warmer at night by the end of the century, it's clear that addressing these issues is crucial for America's biggest cities. In the case of Phoenix, though, the heat island effect keeps temperatures above 37 degrees Celsius at night and ranging from 1 to 3 degrees Celsius higher[86] than surrounding rural areas. But Phoenix is actively making efforts to minimize these effects of climate change. In 2020, the city began testing "cool pavement,"[87] a chemical coating that reflects sunlight and minimizes the absorption of heat to curb the heat island effect. Phoenix has adopted several other sustainability goals[88] as well.

---

[83] https://www.bloomberg.com/news/articles/2021-04-15/transit-agencies-can-make-bikeshare-work-better

[84] https://www.epa.gov/heatislands

[85] https://www.nature.com/articles/s41558-018-0320-9

[86] https://www.taylorfrancis.com/chapters/edit/10.4324/9781315766003-28/holistic-view-effects-urban-heat-island-mitigation-david-sailor

[87] https://www.azcentral.com/story/news/local/phoenix/2020/06/27/phoenix-tries-cool-pavement-pilot-program-curb-heat-island-effect/3247039001/

https://www.phoenix.gov/streets/coolpavement

[88] https://www.phoenix.gov/sustainability

A brighter future means finding solutions at scale, so it's encouraging to see a related idea with big implications from a team of UCLA scientists led by Aaswath Raman; in a bold bid to cool off the planet they have developed a thin, mirror-like film[89] that reflects heat to outer space through radiative cooling, and can lower the temperatures of objects it's applied to by more than 10 degrees. The idea comes from generations of knowledge from people living across desert climates who learned to cool water by simply letting the heat radiate out of it overnight. If this film were applied to pipes and refrigeration units, or added to paint, it could help cool buildings and make refrigeration systems more efficient. That in turn could potentially reduce the need for air conditioning, which is one of the major sources of greenhouse gas emissions[90] and accounts for as much as 70% of residential energy demand in the United States and the Middle East[91]. At the present rates of warming, one study found that by 2050 the cooling devices likely to be used around the world could drive energy usage up to five times what is currently projected[92]. So one of the strongest selling points of innovations like the radiative cooling film is that it doesn't need electricity; it only needs a clear day to do its job.[93] We need more ideas like that, and we need them now.

Taking forward-looking action right now right where we are is what will begin to make brighter opportunities possible. Take for example the trend of green roofs, and in particular the California Academy of Sciences' Living Roof[94]: the museum's roof spans 2.5 acres and runs six inches deep, with an estimated 1.7 million plants, collecting 100 percent of storm water runoff and offering insulation to the building below. The whole endeavor is brilliantly hopeful and strategic.

---

[89] https://www.skycoolsystems.com/about/

[90] https://www.washingtonpost.com/graphics/2019/world/climate-environment/climate-change-qatar-air-conditioning-outdoors/

[91] https://climate.org/cooling-your-home-but-warming-the-planet-how-we-can-stop-air-conditioning-from-worsening-climate-change/

[92] University of Birmingham, "Global quadrupling of cooling appliances to 14 billion could see staggering increase in world's energy consumption – new report," Jul 10 2018. https://www.birmingham.ac.uk/news/latest/2018/07/Global-quadrupling-cooling-appliances-14-billion-increase-energy-consumption.aspx

[93] The Washington Post, "Bringing the chill of the cosmos to a warming planet," Sarah Kaplan, October 7, 2020. https://www.washingtonpost.com/climate-solutions/2020/10/07/radiative-cooling-climate-change/

[94] https://www.calacademy.org/exhibits/living-roof

A massive green roof is completely on brand for a science museum, but that doesn't mean other buildings and businesses wouldn't benefit from them as well. The National Park Service even estimates that over a forty year building lifespan a green roof could save a typical structure about $200,000, of which nearly two-thirds would come from reduced energy costs[95]. This is an area ripe for technological innovation, too: researchers are using machine learning to simulate the runoff from green roofs[96] to estimate their hydrological performance, and using machine learning prediction models to propose an optimization method to minimize the building energy consumption and visual discomfort[97] for a passive building in Shanghai, China.

All of these measures are promising, but we need even more bold new ideas. Those ideas need to be laser-focused on *what is going to matter*. It won't be sufficient to put all our energy into eliminating or cutting emissions based on what we've normalized today; we need true progress, and that's going to take our best, most innovative, most forward-looking efforts. As Tom Steyer writes in the foreword to Paul Hawken's *Drawdown*, "'never again' isn't enough. Humanity needs other, better ideas to take their place."[98]

Climate equity, climate justice

"The best futures for the most people" really comes into play here. In almost every measurable respect, the climate crisis is hitting hardest in poorer communities and marginalized populations, such as Black and Brown neighborhoods in the US and Indigenous populations in countries around the world.

---

[95] National Park Service, "Green Roof Benefits," https://www.nps.gov/tps/sustainability/new-technology/green-roofs/benefits.htm

[96] Abdalla, E. M. H., Pons, V., Stovin, V., De-Ville, S., Fassman-Beck, E., Alfredsen, K., and Muthanna, T. M.: Evaluating different machine learning methods to simulate runoff from extensive green roofs, Hydrol. Earth Syst. Sci. Discuss. [preprint], https://doi.org/10.5194/hess-2021-124, in review, 2021.

[97] Lin Y, Zhao L, Liu X, Yang W, Hao X, Tian L. Design Optimization of a Passive Building with Green Roof through Machine Learning and Group Intelligent Algorithm. Buildings. 2021; 11(5):192. https://doi.org/10.3390/buildings11050192

[98] Steyer, Tom. Foreword. Drawdown: The Most Comprehensive Plan Ever Proposed to Reverse Global Warming. Hawken, Paul. United States, Penguin Publishing Group, 2017. p. viii.

Indigenous communities often have traditional approaches to living gently on the planet and a mindset for cooperating with nature that are well worth learning. Seeking leadership on climate issues from Indigenous people should be a priority.

We know global warming trends and catastrophic weather disasters are going to create waves upon waves of climate refugees. We know famine and drought are likely around the world. And we know authoritarianism and fascism will continue to spring up to calm the fears of people who see too much change happening too quickly. We can't acquiesce to fascism, but we can't slow down change either. We need new ways of talking about and making progress that is inclusive, equitable, bold, and sustainable.

It needs to start today.

We all have actions we can take individually to lighten our footprint on the planet, and we should commit to those wherever we can. But the bigger impacts will come from comprehensive reforms of bigger systems, from transportation to water infrastructure, from food distribution to waste management. We can't wait for these changes to take place gradually over decades. We need bold action on behalf of humanity and the planet by elected leaders, corporate leaders, institutional leaders, and community leaders. And since you *are* a leader, in whatever capacity, that means we need bold action from *you*.

Chapter 15:

Meaningful Work versus Meaningful Jobs

THERE'S SOMETHING FUNNY ABOUT THE way we talk about the future of work. Here's what I've noticed.

The discussions about the future of work have mostly to do with what employment looks like from an employer-oriented lens: what are the roles, what kinds of benefits will people expect, how will work groups function across distributed locations and with increasingly automated components, and so on.

Meanwhile, the discussions about the future of jobs are driven by individuals rather than companies. And they express very different, very human anxieties: about earning a living, providing for oneself and one's family, and so on.

On that side of the discourse, people tend to wonder: What might we each be doing in five, ten, or twenty years? What skills do we need to compete within an increasingly global—not to mention increasingly automated—workforce?

Many if not most of these concerns come down to: How can we ensure that robots won't take our jobs?

Or, perhaps, if they do, how can we ensure that billions of people won't be left to face homelessness and hunger? And we know it sounds bananas, but we kinda have to ask: How can we ensure we won't end up as servants to robots?

And the truth is it no longer sounds alarmist to say that at least some parts of our jobs are probably going to be displaced or replaced by automation or cognitive computing. In fact, depending on the forecast you consult, as many as half of all job categories risk complete replacement by machines.

So we know machines will impact people's employment, as well as the economy, production, efficiencies of scale, and innovation.

We just don't know what any of that really looks like yet.

But as always, we can get a sense of the future by looking at the past and where it has led us.

Under decades of increasing pressure from shareholders, competitors, and an ever-more global marketplace, companies have tended to pursue greater profits and greater growth by continually investing in more efficient methods of achieving results. So if that leads to, say, offshoring to regions where cost of living is significantly lower so the company can pay significantly less for wages, the thought has traditionally been: *So be it.*

And if profitability now points to subsidizing or replacing huge chunks of human labor with robots and other automation, this mindset again suggests: *So be it.*

That sounds like a pretty doom and gloom forecast for human workers, right?

Well, maybe.

But not so fast.

One factor that complicates this narrative is a trend best characterized in August 2019, when Business Roundtable put out a statement saying that the purpose of a company is not just to make profit, but rather to "share a fundamental commitment to all of [their] stakeholders"—which is a position I've argued for a long time.

Another thing: That offshoring trend of the last ten to fifteen years is itself likely to be substantially reshaped by automation over the next three to five. In that case, many call centers will be augmented by increasingly automated systems, which will shift the opportunity again; now the most innovative companies will figure out how to integrate human call specialists and supervisors into that automated system. The resulting work that will fall to humans will increasingly be the tasks that require emotional agility and strong language and communications skills.

It's a complex picture, but it's important to note that adding automation to the workforce doesn't necessarily mean eliminating human jobs. It means machines will continue to augment human jobs, as they've done ever since machines have existed—from drills to calculators, to mainframes, and beyond.

Granted, it would be intellectually dishonest not to state clearly that the scale is different.

And it is true that the rapidly growing capabilities of automation are making it increasingly possible to displace and replace the tasks of human workers.

But the essence of the equation remains: Machines are built to take on tasks —whether for efficiency or for accuracy or for safety—and the set of jobs *that we do* changes as a result. So the main impact of automation and robots is augmentation: of jobs, of work, of the workplace.

In other words, the overall direction of the concerns people feel about the future is totally reasonable, but the reality is more nuanced than "robots are taking our jobs." Rather, as emerging technology augments human jobs, we will also create new and sometimes more interesting human jobs.

That last point is something we don't talk about often enough, and I think it's because it's hard for people to envision those jobs.

So how can we help humans anticipate the jobs of the future and prepare for them and adapt to them when neither they—nor we—can even see what they are yet?

Well, it is for sure going to take new skills in new combinations, but they're not totally mysterious.

As we look ahead in the relatively near term, one thing is clear: Emerging skills in the workplace will be needed for managing combined teams of humans and machines.

Let's say the future of work, from a business standpoint, is automation and robots and algorithmic optimization, and that human involvement is tuning, improving, and aligning. What does that look like in practice?

It looks like using some very human skills that all of us already have to some degree.

And if we look at work as a marketplace not only of *jobs to be done*, but of *value to be added*, it may become a little clearer where humans have a promising future.

After all, jobs to be done are identifiable, discrete units of labor that can be executed by anyone or anything, so we can expect that type of work to be easily automated. But the judgment it takes to size up a situation and break it down into its component tasks is complex, subjective, and nuanced—a trait that is, for the time being, more in line with human capabilities than machine.

And—there is arguably always more value that can be added to a function, service, or product by imbuing it with meaning, which is again something humans are right now better poised to do than machines.

Robotic process automation

We should note, too, that replacing humans from certain kinds of jobs isn't always a decision based on greed: Some robots and other machines can do some jobs more safely and efficiently than human workers, to the point it doesn't make sense to endanger humans in those capacities. This is the case, for example, with some of the tasks in auto manufacturing that have been handed over to robots over the past few decades.

The focus with robots and robotic process automation shouldn't inherently be on efficiency and human worker replacement; rather than thinking in terms of eliminating human workers, we should emphasize how to put humans in the highest-value roles.

The emerging future of the workplace

Of course, we need to take a little detour because COVID-19 has introduced some new wrinkles to this discussion.

So as we've discussed, there is a difference between the future of work and the future of jobs. But there's also a difference between the future of work and the future of the *workplace*.

The workplace is wherever you do your work—maybe at home, at your kitchen table, on your sofa, or on your bed. (I'm not judging.)

The more "official" workplace is understood to be the center of the work—the headquarters, the office, the campus, what-have-you. *This* workplace has a whole new set of requirements thanks to the pandemic, related to its ability to provide for teams that need to be together, to keep people safe, to monitor their safety, to facilitate efficiency so people may be able to show up for a meeting, get that meeting done, and leave—and reduce their time of exposure to one another.

A lesson in what is essential

But just as significantly, the pandemic has also forced revealing discussions about what is "essential" work. It isn't necessarily the kind of work that can be done remotely or in distributed teams. It isn't necessarily so-called "knowledge" work either.

For example, janitorial and other cleaning jobs become critical during a pandemic, as workers ensure that spaces and surfaces are sanitized. Grocery store workers were the essential workers most of us perhaps didn't value quite enough as "essential" before.

And in a pinch, amid unsafe conditions or for any other reason, only some of these job roles could feasibly be entrusted to, say, robotic systems at this point. But that doesn't mean there isn't risk. Many lower-skilled jobs are at risk of displacement, and in many cases, this displacement is already underway; workers need new jobs now, not in some distant imagined scenario.

Reskilling and upskilling

Prior to the pandemic, the fastest-growing jobs were middle-skills jobs that require training beyond high school but not a college degree, according to Georgetown University's Center on Education and the Workforce.[99]

One of the regions with some of the greatest potential employment impact is southern Nevada, where growth in data and call centers as well as transportation and logistics hubs has built an employment base that stands to be heavily impacted by intelligent automation. But in late 2020, the state of Nevada published a comprehensive strategic plan to reinforce, among other areas, relevant education and workplace opportunities, leaning on public-private partnerships as well as relationships with industry, educational institutions, and the public sector.[100]

Meanwhile, the Nebraska Governor's Office of Economic Development has a "Skills Decoder Platform, which is accessible in local libraries and community colleges, that uses immersive technologies to help match displaced, job-seeking individuals with certain employer needs, translating workers' experience into credits" and helping to find relevant opportunities quickly[101].

Too rarely are workers themselves asked what they want to see happen in their jobs, but it seems many people see the opportunity in bringing new technologies into their jobs.

One study showed that employees are excited about the possibilities automation brings (e.g., removing boring/repetitive aspects of roles); that they desire adequate preparation for automation events and the future of automation; that they want strategic on-the-job-support that "gets it right" when automation is implemented; and, in addition to wanting e-training opportunities, that they

---

[99] Georgetown University Center on Education and the Workforce, Three Educational Pathways to Good Jobs: High School, Middle Skills, and Bachelor's Degree, 2018. https://cew.georgetown.edu/cew-reports/3pathways/

[100] Nevada Governor's Office of Economic Development & SRI International, " Nevada's Plan for Recovery & Resilience," December 2020. https://goed.nv.gov/wp-content/uploads/2021/01/Nevada-Recovery-and-Resiliency-Plan-FINAL.pdf

[101] https://goed.nv.gov/wp-content/uploads/2021/01/Nevada-Recovery-and-Resiliency-Plan-FINAL.pdf

desire a collaborative (peer + management) training experience for the future of automation in their jobs.[102]

This reinforces the notion that companies adding automation to their workflow bear a responsibility to include existing workers in training for new sets of skills that are needed to integrate with the new technologies.

Fortunately, this view *does* seem to be largely shared among today's leaders: In a survey of CEOs, two-thirds (67 percent) said they have a responsibility to retrain employees whose tasks and jobs are at risk of being automated out of existence.[103]

One approach to the opportunity for reskilling and upskilling is online training and certification programs. Many corporations in tech and otherwise are turning to MOOCs, or massive open online courses, to both train and attract talent.[104] MOOCs are a driving force behind efforts to democratize education and train more knowledge workers at a lower cost.[105] Aimed at unlimited participation and open access via the Web, these courses were around well before the COVID-19 pandemic, but they have received increased attention given the constraints on traditional educational practices presented by the pandemic. They've come to be seen as a sustaining force in higher education[106], and a needed one; unless we get more high-tech workers by 2030, the US could miss out on over $160 billion of annual revenue.[107]

---

[102] https://sloanreview.mit.edu/article/what-employees-tell-us-about-automation-and-re-skilling/

[103] https://sloanreview.mit.edu/article/what-employees-tell-us-about-automation-and-re-skilling/

[104] EdSurge, "To Attract Talent, Corporations Turn to MOOCs," Wade Tyler Millward, May 24, 2019. https://www.edsurge.com/news/2019-05-24-to-attract-talent-corporations-turn-to-moocs

[105] Harvard Business Review, "Can MOOCs Solve Your Training Problem? Insights from a study of 28,000 learners in 127 countries." Monika Hamori, January–February 2018. https://hbr.org/2018/01/can-moocs-solve-your-training-problem

[106] Ahmed A. Al-Imarah & Robin Shields (2019) MOOCs, disruptive innovation and the future of higher education: A conceptual analysis, Innovations in Education and Teaching International, 56:3, 258-269, DOI: 10.1080/14703297.2018.1443828
https://www.tandfonline.com/doi/abs/10.1080/14703297.2018.1443828?journalCode=riie20

[107] Korn Ferry, "The $8.5 Trillion Talent Shortage," Michael Franzino, Alan Guarino, Yannick Binvel, Jean-Marc Laouchez. https://www.kornferry.com/insights/this-week-in-leadership/talent-crunch-future-of-work

But do these platforms only alleviate fears about being made redundant in the future of work, or do they genuinely help people gain skills and prepare for the future? According to Anne Trumbore, Darden Executive Education & Lifelong Learning Executive Director of Digital and Open Programs, 79 percent of MOOC learners felt they "definitely" or "probably" experienced career benefits from taking MOOCs, including: upskilling; improved job performance, new roles, and raises; preparation for, or supplementary learning during a degree program; and lifelong learning.[108]

If you're looking for the monetary incentive, the World Economic Forum published a report in early 2021 forecasting that "accelerated investment in upskilling and reskilling of workers could add at least $6.5 trillion to global GDP, create 5.3 million (net) new jobs by 2030 and help develop more inclusive and sustainable economies worldwide."[109]

But the humanist argument is convincing too. In his 1974 opus *Working*, an oral history account of American workers, Studs Terkel wrote that working people look for "daily meaning, as well as daily bread, for recognition as well as cash, for astonishment rather than torpor; in short, for a sort of life rather than a Monday through Friday sort of dying."[110] (Obligatory side note: once, in the nineties, I met Studs Terkel while standing in line behind him in a Chicago grocery store in one of the most charming random interactions I've ever had with a well-known public figure. He must have caught me staring at the back of his head and he turned to me and said, in a kind but wry manner: "Yes, dear, it's me.")

In general, in thinking about the transition from today's work to tomorrow's, consider the work that needs to be done as separate from the routines and places through which and in which work has historically been done—and you may see opportunities to decouple legacy expectations of the workplace or of job functions.

---

[108] University of Virginia Darden School of Business, "Preparing for the Future of Work: What Can MOOCs Do for You?" Jay Hodgkins, February 9, 2021. https://ideas.darden.virginia.edu/future-of-work

[109] World Economic Forum, "Investment in Upskilling Could Boost Global GDP by $6.5 trillion by 2030," January 25, 2021. https://www.weforum.org/press/2021/01/investment-in-upskilling-could-boost-global-gdp-by-6-5-trillion-by-2030/

[110] Terkel, Studs. Working: People Talk About What They Do All Day and How They Feel About What They Do. United States: New Press, 2011.

Involve team members to help reimagine their workflow. Some of them are very eager to get back to working in team environments in offices because they thrive in those settings, and others are desperately hoping to stay home after COVID-19 because they thrive in that setting. Whatever the old way was, it most likely doesn't need to be what you return to. You have the opportunity to reinvent teamwork and culture across remote and distributed teams and projects, and the future-ready value that will come from those choices could well be immeasurably huge.

And we need to do this with a sense of urgency for all generations, not just more junior- or entry-level roles, and not just for more senior roles that cost more. One of the great opportunities here is in reframing the nature of work beyond the traditional terminology of job roles. The tasks that comprise various job titles or roles are bound to shift and evolve from here, perhaps more rapidly than ever. The focus could stand to shift more to the value people add through their unique perspectives, skills, experiences, and characteristics.

Universal Basic Meaning

Sometimes people imagine a future where humans don't have to work for money, or at least a future where humans aren't doing routine, mundane, or meaningless jobs for money.

That's admittedly an appealing science fantasy.

But jobs also mean more to humans than money. A job has historically been, at least in part, about identity. About dignity. About accomplishment and achievement.

We have long associated work with what we do. We have long associated work with who we are. Our work can be central to our identities. There's this long tradition of names—last names and family names—being derived from professions: Carpenter, Baker, Butcher, and so many others. And this happens across languages, not just English. We take so much of who we are and what we are about in this world from what we do for a living, and what our ancestors have done for a living.

In other words, humans have traditionally derived tremendous meaning from work.

So I worry about what will happen to us as human jobs shift away from work we can find meaning in. What I think will be needed, even more than ever, are meaningful experiences in the world around us. At scale.

Not to take the place of work. Not to replace jobs.

But because our everyday environments are and increasingly will be driven by data and optimized by algorithms, automated and efficient—will they feel empty or will they help us feel connected to one another and our communities?

When I think about the exponential change of emerging technologies, what I see is the trajectory of experiences becoming increasingly automated, and how often these experiences are selected for automation by how mundane they are—which means that increasingly, we will be surrounded by more mundane and meaningless automated experiences.

In particular, as we think ahead to a world with shifting definitions about jobs and work, we need to think about how we interact with the world at large, how we derive our sense of identity and accomplishment, how we feel fulfillment.

Certainly a lot of people are talking about universal basic income, and what it is going to look like for people not to have the financial resources from working. I'm just as concerned about people not having the resources of meaning and identity.

We need to begin thinking about a society that fulfills us by default, if not as a replacement for what we get from work, then at least as reinforcement. Like a Universal Basic Meaning that's encoded around us.

I believe meaning—universal meaning—is a need possibly even more fundamental to human flourishing than universal employment or universal income.

So this may sound a bit shocking, but bear with me: What matters in the long-distant view of the future is not so much that humans do labor, per se. What matters is that humans have the opportunity and the resources for meaningful experiences in the future, whether we derive them from work or not. So as long as we can make contributions at a level that feels significant to us, as long as we can feel a sense of purpose in our being in the world, we should be able to wholly reinvent our relationship with labor and productivity. Not as a utopian vision of never having to work again, per se, and not only as an answer to the dystopian vision of being replaced by robots—somewhere both/and, of course, but also beyond: an opportunity to reimagine our existence in ways both minute and massive that can reaffirm the human condition, reshape the economy around our most foundational needs, and help us thrive well into the future.

What would Universal Basic Meaning look like?

It's pretty clear that all meaning can never be universal because experiences and perspectives are too personal. But to the extent that experiences out in the world are relevant to our inner sense of experience and meaning (which they are) and to the extent that current experiences resonate with our past experiences and perspectives (which they do), we can build upon that layered understanding. We can identify some of these experience layers, and scaffold up from one level to the next to create a sense of depth and dimension in the transactions and interactions we design and create for others. In other words, where possible, given context and shared history, we can find common ground and common experiences.

For example, as someone who has experienced the deaths of people very close to me, I often find that meeting other people who have lost loved ones forms an instant bond. Almost nothing else matters as much as that bond. I haven't had children, but I have sometimes seen parents connect with each other quickly over having and raising kids, so it seems that shared experience is another type of bond. I have observed it in my friends who were profoundly shaped by parenthood—that they process what is significant in life as it relates to being a parent, much as I process what is significant in life through the lens of having overcome major loss.

In some ways, it almost doesn't matter what your shaping experience is, so long as you've had some kind of shaping experience. But the people whose fundamental shaping experiences are alike can better relate to one another.

Thinking about that connection gives us a clue about where we can go to find one extreme end of the meaning spectrum—when you've encountered the beginning or the end of life in a way that has given you new perspective on life and death itself. So if we peg that all the way to the extreme of the meaning spectrum, on the far "existential" side of meaning, we can perhaps envision what we encounter on the nearer end; we can also recognize meaning that's closer to transactional, that pertains to moment-by-moment relevance, that speaks to a functional purpose in the here and now.

If we distill the many meanings of meaning into their essences and put them in simple terms, we could create a range of perspectives on what is meaningful from micro to macro and back again. The perspectives in this range of meaning might best be expressed in "why" statements, such as:

Why are we here? (Cosmic)

Why am I here? (Existential)

Why am I doing this? (Purpose)

Why does this matter? (Significance)

Why does this pertain to me? (Relevance)

Why am I saying this? (Semantics)

167

Within and across this range of meaning lies the opportunity for experience design and strategy.

I'll give you an example that may feel trite after talking about the profundity of life and death, but it's a helpful illustration of how to bring these lofty insights down to earth and apply them on the ground. When Snapchat rolled out its Spectacles product, they chose to do so at popup events in places like New York City. Making the rollout an event was not revolutionary, but as people had to stand in line, the excitement built in a way that people coming out of the store with the new gadget were able to engage with the line using the product and the platform. People used kiosks inside the stores to obtain the product, and once they had the product in hand they could immediately post about it to the platform, featuring the very visually on-brand environment. Even the storefront itself was on brand and part of the experience, draped in solid yellow to match the logo and brand color. The experience of acquiring the glasses all felt like a dimensional part of the product itself.

These details may seem trivial, hardly worth mentioning in a future-looking book about Strategic Optimism, but that is in fact the point: Even gadgets and everyday consumer objects have the opportunity to be part of an intentionally-designed and incrementally more meaningful landscape when the experiences around them are designed with consideration. Imagine what you can do with your own products and services.

Experience strategy that doesn't include these aspects of dimensionality and purpose is missing tremendous opportunities for ongoing relevance in a future where everything is increasingly connected. The more versed we are with meaning in its many forms, the more we can create human experiences worth having, worth talking about, and that lead us optimistically into a future surrounded by thoughtfulness.

Building a brighter future of work

Given all that we've just discussed about jobs and work, about the workplace, and about the meaning in the world around us:

In the near term, how can companies build a better workplace for humans to thrive in and for technology to bring efficiency and scale to?

Well, it starts with purpose. Strategic, organizational purpose. That should be an articulation in language as plain and clear as possible what it is your company or organization exists to do, and what it is trying to do at scale.

Purpose, of course, is a form of meaning. It is, as we've covered previously, the shape that meaning takes in business. So it's a way to make sure we have a human-centric view of what matters in our work and our workplace.

Purpose should match your values and priorities, your brand, your culture, and even the data model and the technology you deploy to support the organization. By making this purpose accessible and transparent to the people who work in and around your company (perhaps even by involving them in the process of determining how to articulate it), you help them see how their own contributions hook into the larger reason for the organization's priorities, which means you're also helping them make *relevant* contributions that are more effective and more likely to be successful.

Human-Centric Digital Transformation Model

Using that clear sense of strategic organizational purpose to shape the data models you build around your business and the technology you use to amplify and accelerate it is what I call "Human-Centric Digital Transformation." (I delve into this topic a lot more in *Tech Humanist*, by the way.) That term may be a mouthful, but I call it that because digital transformation is driven by human needs and factors, even when we don't realize it. So it's far more effective and clear if we do.

It breaks down like this: Digital transformation, as we tend to talk about it, is primarily about data transformation. And the data in business is largely derived from people: what people want and need, the behavior they exhibit, the relationships they cultivate, and so on.

So it seems only fair and it only stands to reason that as we optimize our processes around the efficient handling of that data and optimize our business models around more and more profitable decisions informed by that data, we should do so in a way that honors and respects the human beings whose data we are building upon.

The new work contract

If we're trying to create purpose-aligned organizations that create meaningful experiences, and we should be, then that human-centricity must shape the values, the culture, and all the decisions that affect the people inside the organization as well as outside the organization. Diversity, inclusion, equity, and belonging can no longer be afterthoughts. For a company to be future-ready, these values and concepts must be front and center in a company's team- and culture-building strategy. Even professionalism and executive presence are both exclusionary concepts by default, unless they've specifically been unpacked to make sure they are inclusive of all races and cultures, all genders, all abilities and disabilities, and so on.

Moreover, we must be able to bring our whole selves to work for mental health in the workplace. The pandemic increased the visibility of the need to talk about and have a plan in place to accommodate stress, burnout, depression, substance abuse, and more. People can only make their best contributions if we are supportive of their authentic needs.

We've all got to be in this together

Trying to create a future of work and jobs and workplaces that promote the efficiency of machines is important, sure, but we also have to imbue business and machines with the best and most meaningful characteristics of humanity, like compassion, context, and good judgment.

Remember, we're facing multiple simultaneous exponential changes from a variety of sources.

The forces are bigger than any of us.

So we've all got to be in this together.

And the more we align business incentives and human values, the better the chances we'll build the meaningful experiences of the future *in* our jobs and *beyond* our jobs, in cities and all the places we live and work and play, in the more purpose-aligned future we build together. The far worse alternative is to accidentally surround ourselves with automated meaninglessness at scale. Let's aim for the bright side.

Chapter 16:

Living and Playing

I wrote a lot about the human relationship to place and our understanding of home in *Pixels and Place*. But one quote I only came across after I published that book in 2016 is from the architect Witold Rybczynski, who connected two of my great loves—place and language—when he said: "This wonderful word 'home', which connotes a physical 'place' but also has the more abstract sense of a 'state of being', has no equivalent in the Latin or Slavic European languages. German, Danish, Swedish, Icelandic, Dutch, and English all have similar sounding words for 'home', all derived from the Old Norse 'heima'."[111]

It's a lovely reminder that our state of being, our home, is a beautifully abstract concept that is interwoven with how we conceive of our identities, our communities, and our sense of security.

To all the things they say begin at home, we can add the work of the brighter futures we seek.

---

[111] Rybczynski, Witold. Home: A Short History of an Idea. New York: Viking Penguin, 1986. p.62.

One particularly interesting aspect of the opportunities ahead is that they rely on humans to come together in place. Communities, cities, regions—at any level of zoom, we can make tremendous advances through collective action in proximity with one another, whether through small-scale agriculture, closed-loop economies, or other systems relevant to the needs of the area. Place is an abstraction with concrete benefits to us.

Jane Jacobs, whose work I deeply admire, begins her treatise *The Death and Life of Great American Cities* by quoting the following unusually long passage from Oliver Wendell Holmes Jr.:

"'Until lately the best thing that I was able to think of in favor of civilization, apart from blind acceptance of the order of the universe, was that it made possible the artist, the poet, the philosopher, and the man of science. But I think that is not the greatest thing. Now I believe that the greatest thing is a matter that comes directly home to us all. When it is said that we are too much occupied with the means of living to live, I answer that the chief worth of civilization is just that it makes the means of living more complex; that it calls for great and combined intellectual efforts, instead of simple, uncoordinated ones, in order that the crowd may be fed and clothed and housed and moved from place to place. Because more complex and intense intellectual efforts mean a fuller and richer life. They mean more life. Life is an end in itself, and the only question as to whether it is worth living is whether you have enough of it.

'I will add but a word. We are all very near despair. The sheathing that floats us over its waves is compounded of hope, faith in the unexplainable worth and sure issue of effort, and the deep, sub-conscious content which comes from the exercise of our powers.'"[112]

This excerpt is from a speech given by Holmes Jr., one of the most eminent legal philosophers in the US and eventually a Supreme Court justice, at a dinner in his own honor in 1900. Jacobs seems to be quoting Holmes to emphasize that life and "enough of it" is, in a sense, the connective tissue of place, of cities, because of the people who inhabit them—resisting despair through the agency of our collective actions made possible by place. Holmes's own words contain both hope and strategy, of sorts, in an "everything is connected" poetic context.

---

[112] Jane Jacobs, *The Death and Life of Great American Cities*. United Kingdom, Knopf Doubleday Publishing Group, 2016. p.2.

Cities get ready to lead the way

"First we shape the cities—then they shape us."

— **Jan Gehl**, *Cities for People*[113]

The majority of the world's population already lives in cities. And while there are certainly those people who find city living daunting and mysterious, and while there are indeed aspects of city living that any city-dweller will be quick to acknowledge as annoying, the world also benefits from the cultures that urban environments are often known for. These result, as much as anything, from the intellectual and creative stimulation of living in close proximity with people from all walks of life, not to mention the shared infrastructure and resources that, in the best cases, make it possible for people to better themselves.

"The fifty largest metros across the globe house just 7 percent of the world's total population but generate 40 percent of global economic activity."

—**Richard Florida**, *The New Urban Crisis: How Our Cities Are Increasing Inequality, Deepening Segregation, and Failing the Middle Class-and What We Can Do About It* [114]

Many of the brightest ideas for the future will also depend on sharing resources, close connections between people, meaningful use of public spaces, and collective action. So it's lucky that more and more people are moving to

---

[113] Jan Gehl, *Cities for People* (United Kingdom, Island Press, 2010. p.9

[114] Florida, Richard. The New Urban Crisis: How Our Cities Are Increasing Inequality, Deepening Segregation, and Failing the Middle Class-and What We Can Do About It. United States, Basic Books, 2017.

cities, and by 2030 the world population living in cities will be nearly 70[115] percent.

Cities are where opportunity is perceived to be. And in fact, cities account for 80 percent of the global GDP, and with the estimated growth in population in the years to come this percentage is likely to expand.[116]

Cities have identities all their own, and these identities both shape their inhabitants and are shaped by them.

New Yorkers are ambitious and talk fast. Parisians are chic. These may be reductive attributes—even stereotypes—but these characteristics in part attract people to visit and relocate to these cities. Working with an awareness of the city's "brand" in the world can give city planners a leg up on the intentional design of future-looking programs.

For example, while the efforts to spur tech startup growth in Paris have resulted in many types of products and companies, one category that has been particularly strong is fashion tech—an obvious fit for a city known the world over for fashion.

Or look at smaller cities with notable brand recognition. Portland, Oregon. Boulder, Colorado. Or the iconic "Keep Austin Weird" campaign that originated in 2000, when Red Wassenich, a librarian, called into a local radio station to make a donation "because it keeps Austin weird."[117] It only really gained traction, though, three years later when Steve Bercu, who owned the bookstore Book People, needed a rallying cry to object to a planned Borders chain store a few blocks away. A popular bumper sticker slogan was born, and Borders never moved in.[118]

---

[115] Future Cities: 42 Insights and Interviews with Influencers, Startups, Investors by Stefano L. Tresca

[116] ibid

[117] https://www.kvue.com/article/news/is-austin-still-weird/269-0680af17-2207-4f64-b2ab-3726ecb1804a

[118] Slate, "Weird's Worth," Elizabeth Devitt and Juli Berwald, September 27, 2016. https://slate.com/human-interest/2016/09/how-weird-became-an-economic-strategy-for-hipster-cities.html

Weirdness of some sort may feel authentic in Austin (or Portland or Santa Cruz, where similar bumper sticker campaigns gained traction[119]), but that term wouldn't be the defining characteristic for every city. That's why it works, and the fact that it doesn't work everywhere is part of what makes city branding so interesting.

Cities and places in general often have strong brand recognition, but in ways that differ from corporate and product branding. Brands in the corporate sphere are all about simplicity, but places are more nuanced and complex, and by extension the image of richness and complexity is part of a desirable meta-attribute for places.[120]

The scholarly article from which that insight derives also points to Barcelona as a particularly strong example of place branding. An emphasis on events in the city as part of the region's overall revitalization story began with hosting the Olympic Games in 1992 and followed with the organization of the World Mobile Congress in 2006. This event-relevant positioning has matured to be able to bring in investors, tourists, and talent across an array of fields: in technology, with Mobile World Capital Barcelona and the Barcelona Tech City hub; in business, with the Barcelona Global lobby; and in sports, with FC Barcelona, and its global following. The article also notes that the success of a place brand draws from the wealth of public input and information and its opportunity to become a "de facto regional strategic plan." Which means that place branding is intrinsically linked to urban planning—and to the region's sustainable development, as well.

For another example, take a look at Louisville, Kentucky—well known in connection with its regional bourbon dominance. The city doubled down on that positioning by offering an "Urban Bourbon Trail" that visitors can access in print or as a smartphone app. In either form, it offers visitors returning from day trips at farther-flung Louisville-area distilleries an itinerary of more than twenty-five in-town establishments that serve a solid selection of bourbons.

Bringing that tourism back into town has helped to shore up opportunities to invest in infrastructure to the tune of $2 billion, such as improvements to the

---

[119] Slate, "Weird's Worth," Elizabeth Devitt and Juli Berwald, September 27, 2016. https://slate.com/human-interest/2016/09/how-weird-became-an-economic-strategy-for-hipster-cities.html

[120] Shirvani Dastgerdi, A., De Luca, G. Strengthening the city's reputation in the age of cities: an insight in the city branding theory. City Territ Archit 6, 2 (2019). https://doi.org/10.1186/s40410-019-0101-4

Kentucky International Convention Center in downtown Louisville and some 1,700 new hotel rooms under construction.[121]

Of course it's not the liquor branding, per se, that makes the story optimistic; it's the integration with broadly meaningful facilities that stand to benefit a wide array of the city's residents through economic expansion, varied employment, creative opportunities for entrepreneurial endeavors, and more. The fact that it all builds on what the city is already best known for is what makes it strategic.

A Strategic Optimist (and indeed a Tech Humanist) approach to cities focuses on fully acknowledging the needs of people first, and then uses integrative tools to solve problems at the right level of scale.

For example, in 2014, São Paulo, Brazil rolled out a 16-year city Master Plan that supports sustainable urban development[122]. The planning process invited open participation through a digital platform for proposals and communication so that any citizen could add comments and suggestions. The areas targeted for improvement include affordable housing, better building maintenance and use, special economic zones to encourage better employment distribution, urban mobility such as bike lanes, sidewalk improvements, and dedicated bus lanes, cultural amenities and preservation of heritage. In 2015, the Centro de Acçao Social por Música community center opened as one of the first buildings included in the plan. The four-story building incorporates a variety of passive cooling and ventilation systems surrounded by an urban farm and terraced green space for the public, and offers transit infrastructure, a music school, and a performance hall.

Achieving competitiveness through collaboration and relevance

Being competitive and attractive to talent are concepts many city advocates think about, but collaboration must also become a goal for city planners. Perhaps the greatest strength cities have is in their ability to pool resources and

---

[121] CNBC, "Booming 2nd-tier cities woo tourists with bourbon, music, culture," Kenneth Kiesnoski, June 7, 2014. https://www.cnbc.com/2014/06/07/urbon-music-culture.html

[122] https://gestaourbana.prefeitura.sp.gov.br/master-plan/

build collaborative efforts. In many cases, that collaboration will in fact lead to even more competitive advantage.

You can see this approach being taken in the growth of China's megacity clusters, such as the Pearl River Delta that includes Hong Kong, Shenzhen, and Macau.

It's not uncommon for cities to play up the successful businesses that headquarter there, but what's more rare is for regions to recognize the cohesive brand opportunities in the aggregate.

A 2018 article in *Forbes* points out that even "'Silicon Valley,' to take a more recent example of successful branding, didn't come into general use as a term until the late 1980s, after nearly 30 years of substantial tech growth in the region."[123] Less cohesive but long-standing examples of collaboration between cities include "partner cities" and "sister cities" programs. The city of Birmingham in the UK, for example, lists on its website a wide variety of partner cities: "Birmingham has a strong and well established history of working in formal relationships with cities from around the world. These relationships are formalised through what is known as 'partner city agreements' with the cities of Lyon in France, Frankfurt and Leipzig in Germany and Milan in Italy. We also have 'sister cities agreements' with Chicago in the United States, Guangzhou in China and Johannesburg in South Africa.[124]"

These collaborations are supported by the International Urban Cooperation Programme[125], which fosters relationships between cities focused on sustainable development. New York City, where I live, for example, is paired up with Barcelona "to work on access to affordable housing through community land trusts, housing finance, disposition of city assets and development of modular housing."

Boston to DC, now colloquially known as the Acela corridor for the express Amtrak train that serves it, has been thought of as a megalopolis since the 1950s when French geographer Jean Gottman noticed that the cities in this range were increasingly sharing people and resources.

From an obituary about Gottman in the *New York Times*:

---

[123] https://www.forbes.com/sites/petesaunders1/2018/03/21/the-value-of-city-branding/?sh=1be64ce92ec0
[124] https://distinctlybirmingham.com/partner-cities/
[125] https://iuc.eu/na/home

"His first view of the area's future was optimistic…

"In spite of fears for the future of Megalopolis expressed by city planners, Dr. Gottmann said the area's future was bright in part because it had an 'extremely distinguished population' that was 'the richest, best-educated, best-housed and best-serviced group of similar size in the world'…

"But in a retrospective in 1975, Dr. Gottmann was to take a more cautious view. He said that many large and growing American and foreign cities were faced with challenges that had not been foreseen. Among them were the unexpected demand for social services in the midst of shrinking employment prospects and increasing human stress."

—Richard D. Lyons, "Jean Gottman, 78, a Geographer Who Saw a Northeast Megalopolis"[126]

Gottman's earlier and later assessments might well have been made together. The advantages and disadvantages of megacity clusters should by now be relatively easy to predict and prepare for.

There is no reason, no reason at all, that we cannot use both/and foresight about our decisions and developments to envision the harms manifesting along with the intentions. We can plan cities intentionally, strategically, and with agility. We can recognize that people move freely between world cities, and strive to make them appeal on their merits.

As a 2020 report on the brand value of global cities noted, "A striking feature of globalization is the constant concentration of capital and knowledge

[126] "Jean Gottman, 78, a Geographer Who Saw a Northeast Megalopolis" by Richard D. Lyons
The New York Times, March 2, 1994, Section B, Page 10
https://www.nytimes.com/1994/03/02/obituaries/jean-gottman-78-a-geographer-who-saw-a-northeast-megalopolis.html

in brand-cohesive cities. Although the land of cities cannot be moved, the talent, capital, and enterprises that make up the vitality of cities change every day, which makes the competition among cities on a global scale increasingly fierce. City leaders have recognized the importance of building a competitive international brand for a city."[127]

That means reconciling the goals of stakeholders like property developers, city planners, tourism advocates, and community activists. And certainly it's not always easy to meet so many seemingly conflicting stakeholder goals at once, but there have been some sizeable developments in recent years that seem to have managed or at least come close. Look, for example, at the Wharf in Washington DC, a 3.2 million square foot waterfront project approved by the city zoning commission in 2013. The new development was designed to revitalize a struggling waterfront area, and since its opening, the Wharf has become a DC destination. The $2.5 billion dollar, twenty-seven-acre development is now home to high-end hotels, a concert venue, a luxury condominium with units priced up to $2.9 million dollars…*and* inclusionary housing.[128] The Wharf was even planned with LEED-ND Gold objectives in mind, which included carefully integrated stormwater management designs.[129]

It's also profitable.

In order to make it work, DC lowered the price for the land and reduced the percentage "of lowest cost housing while permitting more below-market, moderate-income 'work force' units." In other words, the Wharf developed housing across multiple price points, about 30 percent of which are affordable and workforce apartments. (Although to be clear, only 16 percent of the development's housing is for people who are making 30 percent or less of the area's median income.) [130]

Hospitals are another type of development presenting opportunity for innovative design, and a few in Australia have risen to the challenge by building

---

[127] Newswire / AP News, "Global City Lab Releases '2020 Global Top 500 Cities'," December 28 2020. https://apnews.com/article/business-new-york-coronavirus-pandemic-asia-economy-b6b022425df665b1e7d7915d4a786cd2

[128] https://www.nytimes.com/2019/07/09/business/affordable-housing-luxury-development-gentrification.html

[129] https://archinect.com/news/article/65964386/phase-1-of-the-wharf-underway-in-dc-perkins-eastman-leads-as-master-planner

[130] https://ggwash.org/view/66186/the-wharf-development-raises-the-question-how-affordable-is-affordable

new or transitioning existing hospitals to run on 100 percent electricity and/or renewable energy sources and be carbon emissions–free. Adelaide is funneling $685 million into building the nation's first 100 percent all-electric hospital for women and children. It will be connected to an electricity source powered by the state's increasingly renewables-dominated electricity grid or through on-site electricity generation and storage, rather than the state's gas infrastructure.[131]

Similarly, a hospital expansion in Canberra, Australia, will run on 100 percent renewable electricity and is set to be operational in 2024. The impact of this initiative is estimated at 1,886 tons of carbon dioxide emissions that will be avoided annually, which equates to taking 760 cars off Canberra roads per year.[132] These local projects align with the South Australian government's commitment to a 100 percent renewable energy grid by 2030—which is itself an acceleration of an earlier target of sometime in the 2030s.[133]

Housing

Homelessness and housing insecurity are problems that look and feel immense and intractable. On any given night in 2018, for instance, over half a million people were experiencing homelessness in the US,[134] and the recent numbers look just as bad in other parts of the world.[135] Plus, given the forecasts of global population growth and the likelihood that most of that growing population will occupy already-overcrowded cities, this is not a problem that tends to attract a great deal of optimism. The most hopeful perspectives about

---

[131] pv magazine, "Adelaide to deliver Australia's first 100% electric hospital," David Carroll, May 14, 2021. https://www.pv-magazine-australia.com/2021/05/14/adelaide-to-deliver-australias-first-100-electric-hospital/

[132] Chief Minister, Treasury and Economic Development Directorate (CMTEDD), " ACT Government announces first all-electric public hospital in Australia (if not the world)," September 02, 2020. https://www.cmtedd.act.gov.au/open_government/inform/act_government_media_releases/rattenbury/2020/act-government-announces-first-all-electric-public-hospital-in-australia-if-not-the-world

[133] Institute for Energy Economics and Financial Analysis, "South Australia energy minister aims for 100% renewable electricity by 2030," May 8, 2020. https://ieefa.org/south-australia-energy-minister-aims-for-100-renewable-electricity-by-2030/

[134] https://www.hudexchange.info/resource/5783/2018-ahar-part-1-pit-estimates-of-homelessness-in-the-us/

[135] Millennium Alliance for Humanity and Biosphere, "Yet another emerging global crisis- Homelessness," Gioietta Kuo, September 13, 2019. https://mahb.stanford.edu/library-item/yet-another-emerging-global-crisis-homelessness/

the current and future state of homelessness recognize that the issue rests at the dynamic intersection of multiple causes and manifests in unique ways in local places—which means it is up to localities to design innovative solutions to homelessness and servicing the needs of the unhoused.

Austin, for example, has been experimenting since 2018 with blockchain to host the personal records of its unhoused population. In principle the program is similar to what Estonia has done for its entire population: decentralized and moved records to blockchain. But especially for people experiencing homelessness, it's important they have verified identity documents to be accessed reliably anywhere because government agencies and social services all want some kind of identification before administering benefits.

The result is the creation of the app MyPass, an identity app for people experiencing homelessness in Austin. The app is designed not only to give people easier access to the documents that form their "identity," but also to help people overcome their present circumstances by building reputations and overcoming identity insecurity. The design of MyPass has been informed by two years of research, which includes the perspectives of participants who have experienced homelessness.[136]

On the other side of the world, Vienna offers three public housing—or as it's known locally, "social housing"—projects, designed by well-known architects in collaboration with different private-sector developers. Located in downtown Vienna in proximity to public transportation, this housing is government-subsidized and rented out by the municipality or nonprofit housing associations to approximately 62 percent of Vienna's citizens, and private developers who work with the city to build affordable housing must allow the city to rent half of the new apartments to lower-income residents. Anyone earning up to $53,225 a year after taxes is eligible to apply for a subsidized apartment in Vienna. To put that number in perspective, the median gross annual income in Vienna is about $31,000. These housing options are pleasant (there are green spaces integrated into the buildings), affordable (one resident told HuffPost that he pays the equivalent of $350 a month in rent—only 10 percent of his income[137]), and good

---

[136] Blockchain for Social Impact, "How the City of Austin is Combatting Homelessness with Decentralized Digital Identity," Mary Dwyer. https://blockchainforsocialimpact.com/how-the-city-of-austin-is-combatting-homelessness-with-decentralized-digital-identity/

[137] https://www.huffpost.com/entry/vienna-affordable-housing-paradise_n_5b4e0b12e4b0b15aba88c7b0

for the local economy[138]. The design of the housing takes a people-first approach: one "car-free" housing project repurposed a parking lot as a bike repair shop, play areas for children, and some car-sharing bays.

Another publicly subsidized experimental development in south Vienna heats homes using waste thermal water from local hot springs and recycles rainwater to flush toilets and irrigate gardens.

These housing projects have brought Vienna into view as one of the most livable cities in the world[139] with one of the happiest populations. Since Vienna's social housing model was featured at an exhibit hosted by the Austrian Cultural Forum in NYC,[140] US cities have taken notice of the model and seriously considered what it would look like to take a similar approach to public housing and homelessness in their own areas.

Community solutions to community problems

In the aftermath of George Floyd's murder and the subsequent protests around the world, the Minneapolis City Council voted in March 2021 to replace its police department with a newly-created public safety department.[141] And while the issue will not go before the city's voters until November of 2021, after this book's publication, the dual messages this vote sends are that law enforcement reform is sorely needed, and it is up to each municipality to determine how they can best solve the problems they face.

The issues of police harassment and brutality in communities of color are an example of where local solutions are probably best poised to address big needs. Even outside of policing reform, this latter point is a recurring theme in the stories that emerge from cities around the world. One size does not necessarily fit all when it comes to the resources, policies, amenities, and solutions a place can offer its inhabitants and visitors.

Minneapolis also designated "Green Zones"—areas where underserved communities are exposed to high pollution, high poverty, and other social issues

---

[138] https://link.springer.com/article/10.1007/s10901-015-9467-0

[139] https://www.economist.com/graphic-detail/2019/09/04/vienna-remains-the-worlds-most-liveable-city

[140] https://acfdc.org/exhibition-social-housing

[141] https://www.independent.co.uk/news/world/americas/george-floyd-minneapolis-defund-police-force-b1816599.html

—as high priority areas for funding. The city is piloting a Green Cost Share program that offers matching funds for properties that are taking on energy efficiency or pollution reduction projects. This operates in support of BIPOC (Black, Indigenous, and People of Color) initiatives designed to support marginalized communities.

Ability and disability

Inclusive design that takes disabilities into consideration is one of the lenses we see used all too rarely. The sidewalk dining developed in many cities during the COVID-19 pandemic, for example, has been criticized for too often impinging on wheelchair access and other mobility needs. Our challenge is to build future spaces that default to inclusiveness of all abilities.

One of the ways the SDGs have been refined is to point out the ways in which disability awareness and inclusion has been woven into all of the goals, but explicitly eleven times.

As the UN reports:

"Disability is referenced in multiple parts of the SDGs, specifically in the parts related to education, growth and employment, inequality, accessibility of human settlements, as well as data collection and the monitoring of the SDGs."[142]

So over and above thinking about Goal 4, Education, for example, as improving education in general, we should think of making education more accessible and inclusive and make sure we provide the assistance needed for people with disabilities.

Infrastructure and transportation

Vehicle miles travelled have increased steadily since the 1960s[143] despite the evidence that private transport is one of the biggest sources of the world's greenhouse gas emissions. Transportation accounts for 29 percent of US carbon

---

[142] https://www.un.org/development/desa/disabilities/envision2030.html
[143] https://www.bts.gov/content/us-vehicle-miles

emissions and nearly 30 percent of the EU's total carbon emissions. But, of course, people can't just cut out necessary travel, such as going to and from work. That's why many cities are promoting—and subsidizing—creative alternatives to private transport in gas-powered vehicles.

Kansas City offers a hopeful vision of public-private partnership for infrastructure development; the city partnered with its local utility[144] to install a record one thousand charging stations, called Clean Charge Network.[145] The initiative cost around $20 million[146] and is largely funded by area business partners. The Clean Charge Network can support more than ten thousand electric cars and encourages drivers to consider switching to EVs by prioritizing convenience in placement of charging stations and featuring profiles of EV drivers in Kansas City on their website.[147] To decide where to place charging stations, Kansas City Power & Light met with other cities with charging stations, relied on research from ChargePoint, Inc. (the California-based manufacturer of the charging stations), and pursued a variety of businesses, including movie theaters, shopping centers, and universities to serve as host sites for charging stations.[148] Because of these sustainability efforts, Kansas City is attracting new companies and talent.

But the push for EVs in Kansas City is complicated; the state of Missouri has moved to impose EV vehicle fees[149] that are three times higher than what gas-powered vehicle owners pay (though it's claimed that the purpose of these fees is to fill the gap in state infrastructure funding[150] that's created when fewer people are paying fuel taxes). This move has been led by the American Legislative Exchange Council, a think tank advocating policies of limited government, free markets, and federalism.

---

[144] https://www.chargepoint.com/about/news/kcpl-becomes-electric-vehicle-infrastructure-leader-groundbreaking-announcement/

[145] https://cleanchargenetwork.com/the-clean-charge-network/about-clean-charge/

[146] https://www.bizjournals.com/kansascity/news/2015/01/28/kcpl-clean-charge-network-operations.html

[147] https://cleanchargenetwork.com/why-drive-electric/driver-profiles/

[148] https://www.bizjournals.com/kansascity/news/2015/01/28/kcpl-clean-charge-network-operations.html

[149] https://www.cnbc.com/2019/09/11/states-hit-electric-vehicle-owners-with-high-fees-consumer-reports-says.html

[150] https://www.usnews.com/news/best-states/articles/2019-12-30/states-hike-fees-for-electric-vehicle-owners-in-2020

In Paris, the Velib shared bikes are partially publicly subsidized, which has resulted in explosive success of public-private efforts to curb carbon emissions and promote "micro-mobilities."

Twenty-minute cities

When we think about the brighter future, one of the opportunities is to completely reimagine what we thought were constraints and open up the field to more radical and regenerative ideas. That's what is happening within the cities that are envisioning "twenty-minute" neighborhoods. The idea is to make everything a person needs for quality of life—such as shopping, recreational activities, schools, and business services—all accessible within a twenty-minute walk, bike ride, or public transit trip from home.

Melbourne, Australia, for example, plans to create twenty-minute neighborhoods throughout the city by 2050. (It's even part of their master plan.[151]) What might seem counterintuitive at first is that in order for this to occur, neighborhoods must first become more densely populated. The goal is to have at least twenty-five dwellings per hectare, which will better support both local activity and the services in the area. With this in mind, the tactic has to be density plus diversity, meaning some of the land needs to be mixed-use. And of course, there needs to be strong public transportation support as well.

Now Singapore is following suit with an approach to twenty-minute towns within a forty-five-minute city. The backbone of their plan involves public transportation[152]: both revamping it and marketing it to increase the likelihood of its use. This creates more "inclusive infrastructure" to help people move around independently, including those with limited mobility, such as elderly people or those with disabilities.

What's exciting is to see variations on these plans come together throughout the world, prioritizing human-powered transportation (walking, cycling, etc.) and developing transit-forward solutions.

---

[151] https://www.planmelbourne.vic.gov.au/

[152] https://www.lta.gov.sg/content/ltagov/en/who_we_are/our_work/land_transport_master_plan_2040.html

In addition, the idea of a twenty-minute city as a necessity may have been expedited by the COVID-19 pandemic.[153] Micromobility options (like electric bikes, for instance) were already becoming more popular before COVID-19, although the options were often stratified by neighborhoods. New ideation around the twenty-minute city is considering how micromobility may be able to combat the "fear" of public transportation caused by concerns about contamination during the pandemic.

---

[153] https://www.forbes.com/sites/edgarsten/2020/09/17/pandemic-may-accelerate-creation-of-the-20-minute-city/?sh=3f29c883706c

Chapter 17:

Earning and Exchanging Value

WE LIVE IN A WORLD that is more enmeshed by data than ever, and more economically interdependent than ever, partly as a result of that data mesh. The global economy could only become as interconnected as it has with the internet and with the digital transformation of supply chains, providing greater transparency and trackability for goods and services around the world.

A bright future for capitalism?

The Strategic Optimism approach—and my view in general—is not inherently anti-capitalist. It does, however, stand against the excesses of capitalism, against the unprecedented power held by too few, and against market thinking as the solution to all problems. Instead of shrugging fate off to an "invisible hand," Strategic Optimism suggests a bright, shining plan to do better. It looks for a more integrative approach to economic troubles, for a more human-centered approach to the future in general.

After all, the economy is people. Trying to say the "economy" is doing well or doing poorly based on stock market indices is to ignore the simple reality that what the economy measures is people being able to live and work and thrive normally.

Milton Friedman asserted that companies have a fiduciary duty to maximize profits for shareholders in the short-term. But a twist on this perspective comes from Paul Polman, former CEO of Unilever, who argues that this is "too narrow a model of Milton Friedman's old thinking. The world has moved on and these people need to broaden their education with the reality of today's world.

He goes on: "I don't think our fiduciary duty is to put shareholders first. I say the opposite. What we firmly believe is that if we focus our company on improving the lives of the world's citizens and come up with genuine sustainable solutions, we are more in synch with consumers and society and ultimately this will result in good shareholder returns.

"Why would you invest in a company which is out of synch with the needs of society, that does not take its social compliance in its supply chain seriously, that does not think about the costs of externalities, or of its negative impacts on society?"[154]

Darren Walker, president of the Ford Foundation, has made similar arguments: "If capitalism is to be sustained, we must intentionally put the nail in the coffin" of Friedman's neoliberal orthodoxy. According to Walker, this approach created a sort of "ideological scaffolding" that deepened inequality. And in the post-COVID-19 world, "many of the norms and understandings and structures of that world…must be reorganized and dismantled."[155]

The metrics that guide these efforts must be holistic and long-term.

It's a weird time, generally speaking, when it comes to concepts of money and value, between meme stocks and NTFs and what have you. And maybe that's good! Maybe that gives us the chance to imagine radical new futures. The stock market in general is kind of a weird notion when you think about it.

---

[154] The Guardian, "Unilever's Paul Polman: challenging the corporate status quo," Jo Confino, April 24, 2012. https://www.theguardian.com/sustainable-business/paul-polman-unilever-sustainable-living-plan

[155] Delivering Social Justice in the Recovery, WEF, https://www.weforum.org/events/the-davos-agenda-2021/sessions/delivering-social-justice-in-the-post-COVID-recovery-2

Proponents of /r/WallStreetBets and meme stocks point to their role in challenging the institutionalized role of finance. (This is sometimes referred to as DeFi, but that term is mostly associated with cryptocurrencies[156].) Retail investors account for about 25 percent of the stock market, but they don't have the same access to information that hedge funds and other financial institutions do. Meme stocks give them the ability to invest in ways that actually impact the market, creating what is essentially a populist movement against Wall Street itself.[157] Additionally, there's (very) new research suggesting that meme stocks—and those who invest in them—may actually improve market efficiency.

And then of course there's Bitcoin and cryptocurrency. One of the hopeful ways to think about this emerging space is that it offers accessibility and decentralization, which is particularly meaningful in parts of the world with greater financial instability[158] or where large populations are unbanked, which is a broad term that characterizes a substantial percentage of the world's population.[159]

Another increasingly popular topic is universal basic income, but as important as it is to experiment with that model and learn what benefits it might have for our future, it also puts more people on an unequal, "dependent" end of the value spectrum or equation and concentrates more power into the hands of fewer people.

So it's useful here to think about how we can champion the intrinsic sense of value and worth of human beings, and how we can understand the meaning that's wrapped up in value.

Cash is becoming increasingly obsolete, and that has inequitable outcomes. Many small businesses see it as good news, giving them less administrative overhead with daily cash management and lower risk of theft, but it's bad news

---

[156] CoinDesk, "What is DeFi?" September 18, 2020. https://www.coindesk.com/what-is-defi

[157] Business Insider, "Retail traders make up nearly 25% of the stock market following COVID-driven volatility, Citadel Securities says," Ben Winck, July 9, 2020. https://markets.businessinsider.com/news/stocks/retail-investors-quarter-of-stock-market-coronavirus-volatility-trading-citadel-2020-7

[158] Philipp Sandner, "The Impact of Crypto Currencies on Developing Countries," Philipp Sandner, Jan 21, 2020. https://philippsandner.medium.com/the-impact-of-crypto-currencies-on-developing-countries-dce44c529d6b

[159] Acuant, "The World's Unbanked Population," November 25, 2020. https://www.acuant.com/blog/the-worlds-unbanked-population/

for vulnerable people who have little access to electronic forms of payment. Older people, the unhoused, and the unbanked all rely on cash, and the move away from cash puts strain on their ability to perform day-to-day functions.

But banks and especially central banks have been looking into central bank digital currencies[160] (or CBDCs) that would be similar to cash—and unlike cryptocurrencies, they would be less volatile, less speculative, and might even offer a solution to unbanked people.

A major move to introduce CBDCs could actually disrupt the financial system. Efforts to introduce CBDCs are gaining momentum, with as many as 86 percent of the world's central banks exploring digital currencies.[161] A 2020 survey from the Bank for International Settlements indicated that nearly every central bank in the world at least did some work on these digital currencies. Some 60 percent are working on "proof of concept" testing, though just 14 percent have actually launched a pilot program or are in development.[162] The move to introduce CBDCs has so far been led by China and the Bahamas, and the Swedish Riksbank is testing a pilot version of a digital krona, or e-krona, that could keep the functions of a currency backed by the state. These moves have motivated Wall Street to consider adopting CBDC as well (even if the Federal Reserve is likely still several years away from developing its own) and to begin an exploratory experiment in partnership with MIT.[163] The more the US embraces these financial innovations and industries of the future, the more the prospects of scaling internet-level prosperity and access become possible. Proving regulatory clarity and a national industrial policy that embraces

---

[160] Peterson Institute for International Economics, "How are central bank digital currencies different from other payment methods?" Martin Chorzempa,
April 21, 2021. https://www.piie.com/research/piie-charts/how-are-central-bank-digital-currencies-different-other-payment-methods

[161] CNBC, "Wall Street banks brace for digital dollars as the next big disruptive force,"
Jeff Cox, April 21 2021. https://www.cnbc.com/2021/04/19/central-bank-digital-currency-is-the-next-major-financial-disruptor.html

[162] Bank for International Settlements, "Ready, steady, go? – Results of the third BIS survey on central bank digital currency," Codruta Boar and Andreas Wehrli, Monetary and Economic Department, January 2021. https://www.bis.org/publ/bppdf/bispap114.pdf

[163] CNBC, "Wall Street banks brace for digital dollars as the next big disruptive force,"
Jeff Cox, April 21 2021. https://www.cnbc.com/2021/04/19/central-bank-digital-currency-is-the-next-major-financial-disruptor.html

exponential technologies such as blockchain can make all facets of the US economy more resilient, future-proof, and competitive.

The Economy Is People

I'm not an economist by education—as I've previously mentioned, I was a linguist—so it has taken me a few years and a lot of reading to arrive at what seems like an obvious statement in retrospect:

The economy is people.

This fuzzy concept we call "the economy" is about a system of tools that enable people to provide for themselves, that measure how well people are able to shelter and feed themselves, and how much people are able to invest back into their own well-being.

You could say that this statement is the "everything is connected" of economic ideas. It sounds simple and self-evident, but it's the layers of its truth that give it revelatory impact.

The COVID-19 crisis has robbed the world of so much, but I do have to thank the crisis for teaching me so clearly that the economy is people—both in terms of our well-being and our productive output. Also planet, as in the state of nature and natural resources. I hate that I spent so much of my life thinking of the "economy" as merely a monetary abstraction.

Measuring a human health crisis in terms of dollars makes no sense. We should be measuring it in terms of human lives impacted, in terms of human potential cut short, in terms of human experiences thwarted. But those are more nebulous figures, and somehow less motivating in a boardroom.

If we are to be proponents of capitalism, as I'd venture many of my readers are, then capitalism must be about solving people's problems in alignment with a focused business objective.

The economy, then, should really be a measure of how efficiently people's problems are solved. And we can apply this to discussions of the various subeconomies: the sharing economy, the gig economy, the knowledge economy. At the end of the day, what we're talking about in every case is people: The economy is built on people.

Capitalism alone is not a tool for the future. We can't entrepreneur our way out of this.

I'm not an adherent of the cult of the entrepreneur anyway, nor the cult of technology, the cult of capitalism, or the cult of scale. All of these otherwise fine ideas become toxic at a certain point.

But I do relate to this:

> "Every time you want to make any important decision, there are two possible courses of action. You can look at the array of choices that present themselves, pick the best available option and try to make it fit. Or, you can do what the true entrepreneur does: Figure out the best conceivable option and then make it available."
>
> —**Jon Burgstone and Bill Murphy**, *Breakthrough Entrepreneurship*[164]

The economy, at the end of the day, is people, and we have to understand that we cannot separate these abstract concepts of whether the economy is flourishing from whether people are flourishing.

Globalism versus place

In thinking about value, the realities of global economics and politics confront us. We once again have a both/and moment in our dual obligations to place and to global community.

It is in our best interest to strengthen our local communities while we also think in terms of global impacts and global citizenship. There's that old adage to "think globally and act locally"; now we could almost twist it to "think locally and act globally."

As feminist and social geographer Doreen Massey has said around this topic: "If space is really to be thought relationally…then 'global space' is no more than the sum of relations, connections, embodiments, and practices. These things are utterly everyday and grounded even as they may, when linked together, go around the world. Space is not the outside of place, it is not abstract,

---

[164] Burgstone, Jon, and Murphy, Bill. Breakthrough Entrepreneurship: The Proven Framework for Building Brilliant New Businesses. United States, Farallon Pub., 2012.

it is not somehow 'up there' and disembodied. Yet that still leaves a question in its turn: How can that kind of groundedness be made meaningful across distance?"[165]

If nothing else, we must recognize that there's no place for xenophobia in the future we face, no place for ignoring how human beings suffer in other places and need our help. The brightest future must be inclusive, and that cannot be ignored.

---

[165] Massey, 2004, "Geographies of Responsibility," Geografiska Annaler 86(1)

Chapter 18:

A Brighter Future for Privacy

"AT THE END OF THE whole day of working with people you want some privacy."

—**Bill Bruford,** drummer and founding member of the prog rock band Yes

As always, we can start by acknowledging the fullness of the truth:

The notion of personal data privacy is endangered, but we have a few good options on the table for how to protect it. That's because for years and years now, each and every one of our purchases, interactions, and even movements through place and space has been designed to generate a volume of data that can be collected, optimized, and monetized at every turn. Many businesses in the last few decades have been built on a model where access is free, such as search engines and social media, because the data our participation generates is valuable enough through advertising and related services to make the companies among the wealthiest and most powerful in the world.

That's one set of challenges, but then remember to figure in the data leaks and breaches that occur near-daily from financial institutions, retailers, political organizations, and just about every kind of entity imaginable. These incidents often include the theft of lists or databases of names and passwords and sometimes other data fields, which can be used to attempt identity fraud or to find additional vulnerabilities in other sites. You can see what tremendous security risks exist and are growing every day because of the richness and complexity of our personal data.

Adding to all of that is the growing use of biometrics, such as fingerprint scans and facial recognition. These present some new and thorny issues for privacy; after all, you can change your password but you can't change your face. We'll get into those issues in more detail soon.

All of this is made more complicated by the disproportionate money and power that accompany this much data; individually, our data is worth relatively little, but across the user base of a popular platform, it can be worth billions. Corporate leaders are then in a conflict of interest, and governments have so far been only occasionally effective in regulating and exercising those regulations.

So where does that leave us? What does Strategic Optimism suggest we do here?

What matters and what is going to matter with privacy?

First of all, corporations need to take an accountable role here. Don't collect more data than you need. The world has begun to wake up to the powerfully disastrous consequences of human data collection and algorithmic optimization at scale—and the biases that can be amplified.

Every company that collects data to do business—which is nearly every company—should have a person or a team that oversees responsible data.

This is another reason why purpose matters: because it's no longer enough to collect human data for data collection's sake. Your data collection should relate to your purpose.

Transforming our understanding of privacy

There's already been a massive shift in the way we think about and talk about data within the past few years. In the mid-2010s, for example, much of the industry discourse was about data sharing, open data, "data is the new oil." But starting in the later 2010s, as more and more people began to see the aggregate impact of data, the conversation turned to data privacy, data protection, and "own your data" movements.

We have a new understanding of openness, and even what we consider being transparent, authentic, and public about our lives is still a curated set of social media posts.

Don't get me wrong: There's still value in opening certain kinds of data—institutional, infrastructural data shared openly through APIs. NOAA, for example, shares weather data through an API, and companies can incorporate that in all kinds of ways.

But the kind of data we are increasingly wary of is personal data.

On an individual level, you can think of your data as a currency. Don't spend it foolishly.

Digital norms are evolving

Digital culture is growing up. Depending on when you started measuring, digital culture is now either drinking age or middle age.

There are certain ideas we have accepted as common sense, such as "What gets measured gets managed" or "If you're not paying, you are the product." The first casually suggests that only what is measurable is possible to manage. The second waves off advertising-based business models as inevitable.

After all, back in the day, it was common for people to use the expression "if you're not paying, you're the product" semi-dismissively, as if we should all just accept that. But as behavioral targeting and such have increased and gotten more laser-pointed, how harmful this equation becomes at scale has become more evident. That idea has become a flippant dodge to a system of problems.

In the early days when all we meant by that was you're going to have to put up with seeing a little advertising in your MySpace, it was *perhaps* innocent enough.

But now when the ad model props up the majority of the content platforms and behaviorial targeting and filter bubbles and and and...it's grown beyond a mildly ominous idea and now represents a threat to media integrity, democracy, and more.

Internet companies are no longer "disruptive" in the upstart sense they once were thought to be. They now represent the infrastructure. The establishment. The leading players—Google, Facebook, Amazon, Netflix, etc.—have been around for decades and have tremendous financial assets, massive user bases, mighty political power, and untold leverage in every useful way.

We have to evolve beyond "common sense" nuggets like "you are the product" with critical thinking that is up to speed and future-ready.

Human data at scale

Meanwhile, let's be clear: The conversation about "digital transformation" is really a conversation about data connectedness. And the vast majority of that data is somehow about or measuring or collected around human experience. The things we do, the things we say, the connections we have, the relationships we have, everywhere we go—all of that gets collected, aggregated, and used by business, governments, and other entities to *determine* our human experiences.

Even the decisions we make about what data to share have repercussions on the data that shapes our identity, and the avatars of people assumed to be like us. Privacy has typically been thought about from a personal, individual sense, but perhaps even more critically, because of predictive inferences[166] that can be made with big data analytics and AI from even incomplete data, your behavior shapes models that can also be used to model and predict other people's behavior.

As systems increasingly come online that can integrate data sets from disparate places, we can fundamentally never fully know what is known about us. Our collective data can be accessed, collected, modeled, predicted, and further built into interactions in ways that can "nudge" us through addiction

---

[166] A RIGHT TO REASONABLE INFERENCES: RE-THINKING DATA PROTECTION LAW IN THE AGE OF BIG DATA AND AI, Columbia Business Law Review – Vol. 2019 – Issue 1,
Sandra Wachter* & Brent Mittelstadt**
Oxford Internet Institute, University of Oxford

algorithms to cooperate and sometimes unwittingly play into a larger scheme of data collection.

When we look at it that way, data shows us just how connected we are—with each other and with our past and future selves. You're connected to your own destiny, to your own past actions, and to your own future in ways that were never as fixed before. Moreover, our everyday human experiences increasingly generate data, and in tandem, our everyday human experiences are increasingly determined by data and optimized by algorithms. The trails of data we leave behind us become a feedback loop of our future opportunities and our digital and physical surroundings that conform to our stated and unstated preferences and worldviews.

Re-imagining our relationship with data

As people become more aware of the vast amounts of personal data they generate with every interaction and how that data shapes their lives, a variety of approaches have emerged to reframe the data relationship and reimagine how we go forward.

"Own your data" movements

The movement for people to own their data has attracted some momentum, as well as some high-profile advocates. They range from Will.I.Am of Black Eyed Peas, who wrote an op-ed in the *Economist* in 2019 advocating for people to be compensated for their data[167], to Brittany Kaiser, cofounder of the Own Your Data Foundation[168], who is best known for being a whistleblower in the Cambridge Analytica scandal following her role in the organization, as profiled in the Netflix Original documentary *The Great Hack*.

Data sovereignty

One promising approach is training more indigenous data scientists. That's the approach of IndigiData, a four-day remote workshop that took place for the first time in June 2021. Krystal Tsosie, who is a genetics researcher at Vanderbilt University and a member of the Navajo Nation, helped to organize the event.

Selective minimalism, selective transparency

The rule of thumb since I've been online has been to never assume what I say or share is ever private or will ever remain where I said or shared it. Even in a social network where your settings are private and you carefully select your

---

[167] https://www.economist.com/open-future/2019/01/21/we-need-to-own-our-data-as-a-human-right-and-be-compensated-for-it

[168] https://ownyourdata.foundation/

friends who have access, someone could still take screen shots of your content, someone could hack their way in, someone could see your content on someone else's screen, and so on.

You can be transparent about yourself and about your preferences in contexts where you feel like the trade-off makes sense.

Start by being selective about the platforms you are on. Many people will tell you to get off of Facebook, for example.

At a minimum, use the On This Day feature on Facebook to go through your archive day by day. You can change the permissions on old content, or delete a post completely if it seems like it no longer serves you to have it out there.

Set up a recurring reminder on your calendar to do an audit of your online presence. I do a weekly glance, a quarterly review, and an annual audit. For the weekly session, you can assign yourself one platform each week, and review your security settings and old content to make sure nothing is out there that you no longer want to share.

Sharing information online with friends and family is fine, but playing into a game or meme that calls for sharing specific data in a structured way is the kind of thing to be hesitant about.

When it comes to smart home devices like smart speakers listening passively for a command, the standards and precedents are not yet well defined for the use and protections of the data those systems collect. The safest thing to do is hold off on using them, and the second-safest thing is to turn them off when not in use.

We're learning how important it is for us to be mindful of our ecological footprint; at the same time, we must learn to be mindful of our digital footprint.

Regulation as a public good

Regulations are often defined as legislation that protects public goods, but to those who oppose regulations, they're also commonly seen as government hindrance and intrusion.

It's understandable that some people oppose regulations on principle. They want a more libertarian (whether that's with a small *L* or large) approach to capitalism, and they don't want small business owners in particular to suffer the indignities of excessive bureaucracy. To be fair, no one really wants the vision of the future where the family business or small business is unable to function due to ungainly regulations and bureaucracy. But the small business owner just isn't the subject of most of today's and tomorrow's pressing needs for regulation.

We have to recognize two things:

1) Quite a few businesses today operate at scales larger than many governments. We live in an era when some corporations could be worth multiple billions or even a trillion dollars, and they have all the political leverage and all the advertising power and all the personal data and all of the reins over all the employees. It's just a lot.

And:

2) People as a whole do need protection from profit-maximizing moves that would threaten their safety.

Amid the rise of technology, business has enjoyed a period of deregulation that has often translated to overreach and should be reined in with regulations that are designed to protect human interests. Merely propping up business with feel-good methodologies about purpose and optimism could be considered tantamount to caving in and surrendering the side of human justice. It's one thing to debate individual liberty versus public health, say, or the arguable community value of surveillance technology. But to oppose regulations in business as a whole amounts to giving too much power to corporate personhood. Human-protective policies and regulations *are* sorely needed in many of the areas we're discussing throughout Part Five: The Brightest Futures: Applying Strategic Optimism. And—not but; *and*—while business continues to have such tremendous reach into our lives, the most urgently human-centered thing to do is to equip business with an approach to developing better technology and engaging in better global citizenship for the good of all humanity and the future of the planet.

To secure the best futures for the most people, we must use the tools that are best able to offer the best protections. We already have financial regulations that protect consumers, as well as regulations around environmental stewardship, ensuring clean air and water, and protecting other public goods.

In the areas of technology and data, as well as in every respect where human flourishing is threatened by the scale of business leverage, we need thoughtfully-created regulations that are themselves a public good.

Given all this, is regulation the only thing that can save us from the absurdity of scale that disconnects us from a better and more meaningful future? We will probably have an ongoing need for more and smarter regulation, but can we also do something more proactive? Can we advance an entirely new worldview?

We need to push for better regulations. The United States is behind on regulating individual data. But individuals need to get savvier too.

Just as with climate action, the experts tell us that we need big movement from commercial and industrial sources in order to see results, but that doesn't mean individuals shouldn't recycle. There are micro effects and macro effects when it comes to privacy and security online.

In addition to regulations, we need to be open to discussions of anti-trust, potentially breaking up big companies, and unions and collective action that favor employees. Instead of groaning when we think about these contentious topics, we need to see them as exciting areas to explore for the future, full of opportunity for vigorous debate.

Don't give machines too much power

Facial recognition specifically

While facial recognition is a subset of the applications of artificial intelligence, it deserves its own treatment. It's not only problematic because of inaccuracy, but also because it exemplifies the kind of overreliance on technology that happens when systems of power latch onto a way to exercise that power more efficiently.

Academic studies—including this landmark 2018 intersectional study conducted by MIT[169]—have found that darker-skinned people are more likely to be misidentified. The MIT study found that:

"The intersectional error analysis that targets gender classification performance on darker female, lighter female, darker male, and lighter male subgroups provides more answers. Darker females have the highest error rates for all gender classifiers ranging from 20.8%–34.7%."

Other studies[170] have confirmed or found consistent results, i.e. that certain demographics are significantly less likely to be correctly identified by facial recognition software than others.[171]

---

[169] http://proceedings.mlr.press/v81/buolamwini18a/buolamwini18a.pdf

[170] https://nvlpubs.nist.gov/nistpubs/ir/2019/NIST.IR.8280.pdf

[171] https://sitn.hms.harvard.edu/flash/2020/racial-discrimination-in-face-recognition-technology/

There are some grave examples of facial recognition software misidentifying a person with some pretty serious consequences. The *New York Times*[172] covered the story of Robert Julian-Borchak Williams, who was arrested in Detroit for felony larceny based on facial recognition software. He was arrested in front of his wife and children, taken to the police station, and accused of robbing a Shinola store. When the officers compared his face to the facial recognition software's photo, they admitted "the computer got it wrong." And yet, Williams was detained for thirty hours before he was released. In April 2021, Williams filed a lawsuit against the police department.[173] The *New York Times* article also includes this stunning statistic:

> "In Michigan, the DataWorks software used by the state police incorporates components developed by the Japanese tech giant NEC and by Rank One Computing, based in Colorado, according to Mr. Pastorini and a state police spokeswoman. In 2019, algorithms from both companies were included in a federal study of over 100 facial recognition systems that found they were biased, falsely identifying African-American and Asian faces 10 times to 100 times more than Caucasian faces."

Given the tendency to misidentify people of color, as you can imagine, Williams's case isn't the only situation where a person of color has been misidentified. Even a Detroit roller-skating rink kicked out a teenager named Lamya Robinson because facial recognition software misidentified her.[174]

In general, the use of this trend by law enforcement is worrying, but what's also troubling is the casual slide into surveillance culture we individuals are making on our own. People using smart doorbells are often capturing video of people not just at their own doorstep but well beyond their property, such as on

---

172 https://www.nytimes.com/2020/06/24/technology/facial-recognition-arrest.html

173 https://www.washingtonpost.com/technology/2021/04/13/facial-recognition-false-arrest-lawsuit/

174 https://gizmodo.com/black-teen-kicked-out-of-roller-rink-because-its-face-r-1847306558

sidewalks, and then that video surveillance is sometimes shared with neighborhood watch communities like Nextdoor or Citizen or with law enforcement.

Beyond misidentification, the hazards of using faces or fingertips or any other parts of our bodies for identity or access is that in the case of hacked, leaked, or breached data, people can't simply change their biometric information like they might change a password.

Fight for the Future[175] has fought to ban facial recognition technology and has delivered two successful campaigns, one that achieved a ban on facial recognition from US concert venues and live music festivals, and another that convinced sixty colleges and universities to commit to not using the technology on their campuses.[176] On their website, Fight for the Future promotes digital and civic literacy by providing a digital copy of a bill for facial recognition regulation, an interactive map showing where facial recognition surveillance is happening, a "congressional scoreboard" tracking who has and hasn't supported the bill, and a form to use to contact lawmakers.[177]

People who are bullish on facial recognition technology's potential talk about how secure it is (think: face unlock on a phone), how convenient it is (think: speeding through customs for an international flight), and how it has other compelling use stories, such as being used to identify missing children. Except that in every one of those cases, there is a nightmare counter-scenario, and they all assume a level of ever-present surveillance culture that renders privacy moot.

The problem is, the technology far outstrips any protections we have in place for it.

With many technologies that have privacy trade-offs, there are options to opt in or opt out. With widespread use of surveillance and facial recognition, if you travel into an area where it is in use, there is no way to opt out.

In the UK, a project in South Wales by Met Police deployed facial recognition broadly in streets and public spaces. In August 2020, however, the UK Court of Appeal unanimously reached a decision against[178] the system,

---

[175] https://www.fightforthefuture.org/
[176] https://www.bbc.com/news/technology-49647244
[177] https://www.banfacialrecognition.com/
[178] https://www.judiciary.uk/judgments/r-bridges-v-cc-south-wales/

calling it "unlawful"—which left some interpretation about the legality of facial recognition technology in the UK as a whole.

We need privacy laws that take biometrics into account. Illinois, for example, in 2008 enacted the Biometric Information Privacy Act of Illinois, or BIPA[179]—one of the toughest privacy laws in the United States. It protects people from their biometric details being used without their consent, say, by the technology companies behind voice assistants or photo recognition services. The law also requires data minimization, or for companies to limit the data they collect, just as the European Union's General Data Protection Regulation Law does. What's more, the law allows individuals, not just the state, to sue companies. Many experts cite it as the exemplar for privacy laws and regulations.

Facial recognition technology is legitimately amazing and also should not advance in most contexts—certainly not in public spaces. There needs to be greater adoption of laws prohibiting it, with regulations protecting individuals whose faces have been recognized in contexts that would otherwise be inadmissible. Once we have the protections in place, we can look with hope at the conveniences it might afford, and what other good it could do for us.

---

[179] https://www.ilga.gov/legislation/ilcs/ilcs3.asp?ActID=3004&ChapterID=57

Chapter 19:

A Brighter Future for Education

WHAT WOULD IT TAKE TO make the future brighter for education? Most teachers and administrators I have spoken with in the US will start their answer with "budgets" and move on to "curricula." And those are very real limitations, but more fundamental challenges are facing education, and many of them are globally relevant discussions.

I'll admit my bias upfront: I hope to see public education expanded and improved everywhere around the world, but particularly in my home country. I'm a product of public schools and state universities, for which I'm grateful, and I have gladly and proudly given back to public education institutions by serving on advisory boards (such as for Tennessee State University, the only public historically Black university in Tennessee, on their Business and Information Systems advisory board) and donating time and money where possible to help fledgling and struggling programs. Educating the public is one of the simultaneously most basic and most honorable functions of civilized society as I see it.

But as we look at the challenges and Change Factors faced by schools and teachers, we see a lot to overcome. College has become prohibitively expensive. Daniel Bignault of WBIR-TV in Knoxville calculated the increases in in-state tuition at the University of Tennessee compared with wages over a nearly forty-year span and found that "from 1982 to 2018, college costs at UT grew by 1430%, while median income grew by 213%, and minimum wage grew by 116%."[180] The return on investment is too uncertain for many students. Given the combination of those factors, the total amount of student debt carried by people well out of school is far too high.

Moreover, the inequity of resources available to students in various neighborhoods and communities leaves far too many kids from lower-income backgrounds, which includes a disproportionate number of students of color, at a tremendous disadvantage.

That's not even to address the environment many young people face when they go to school, with the risk of school shootings having helped drive up the presence of police and private security, even at the expense of more academically-oriented resources, like guidance counselors. Public schools in New York City have over five thousand full-time police officers but just over three thousand guidance counselors.[181] In turn, that police presence drives up the punitive policing of Black and Latino students, and it all feeds into the school-to-prison pipeline. Black students are four times more likely than white students to be charged[182] in cases where police officers respond to incidents—in some cases for adolescent conduct, like burping or cursing.

But even turning our eyes more toward the academics, the offerings in many schools don't keep up with contemporary technology skills, aren't as inclusive as they could be, and don't encourage students to learn the best ways to learn.

Online schools and supplemental education programs that have emerged can offer more personalized matches of skills and curricula, but not all students have access to the computers and broadband needed to use these resources. Of course COVID-19 already limited access to in-person education. In April 2020,

---

[180] WBIR, "College costs vs. income: how they've risen," Daniel Bignault, January 28, 2020. https://www.wbir.com/article/news/education/how-much-college-costs-have-risen-over-the-years-compared-to-income/51-f36aab32-66d7-449a-9067-db48fd1278ca

[181] ACLU, https://www.aclu.org/report/bullies-blue-origins-and-consequences-school-policing

[182] Ibid.

UNESCO reported that in response to the pandemic, 192 countries had closed all schools and universities, which left nearly 1.6 billion children and young people (representing more than 90 percent of the world's learners) scrambling to adapt —as well as their teachers and parents and guardians. The massive shift also raised issues around what happens both to the quality of education and to the loss of education when classes move online. Drawing a comparison to the impact of the 2005 earthquake in Pakistan, Brookings reports that "while children missed three months of school, four years after the earthquake, they were the learning equivalent of 1.5 years behind where they would have been with no earthquake."[183] The impacts were not equally distributed: Around the world, girls' educations were most at risk, with over eleven million girls at risk of not returning to school after COVID-19 due to caregiving demands, early and forced marriages, adolescent pregnancy, and other factors.[184]

There's still a need for ensuring the public has access to the basics of education. The spillover benefits of public education may be hard to quantify, but society stands to benefit from investments in education both in terms of economic prosperity and overall quality of life.

So what will it take to improve education and move us toward the brighter future? There are other resources on this that go significantly further, but consider this list a starting point:

Invest in educating girls worldwide. UNESCO lists several compelling statistics on their website that demonstrate the value of education at the individual level ("just one more year of school can increase a girl's earnings, when she is an adult, by up to 20%") and at the more macroeconomic level ("some countries lose more than US $1 billion a year by failing to educate girls to the same level as boys").[185]

Actively work to remove racism and other systemic discrimination from the curriculum and the classroom, and increase the messages of inclusion and respect.

---

[183] Brookings, "How much learning may be lost in the long-run from COVID-19 and how can mitigation strategies help?" Michelle Kaffenberger, June 15, 2020. https://www.brookings.edu/blog/education-plus-development/2020/06/15/how-much-learning-may-be-lost-in-the-long-run-from-covid-19-and-how-can-mitigation-strategies-help/

[184] UNESCO, https://en.unesco.org/covid19/educationresponse/girlseducation

[185] Ibid.

Reimagine the delivery methods to redress education loss from COVID-19. One model, called Teaching at the Right Level (TaRL)[186], attempts to sort students based on their learning level rather than their age. The method was pioneered in India and rolled out to ten African countries by mid-2020[187]. Whatever the approach, we will clearly need bold and imaginative ideas to make up for the academic losses students around the world will have suffered from the pandemic.

Keep trying to improve the learning opportunity with technology. Learning in person has tremendous advantages, but as an adjunct to that or for students who excel in remote learning environments, the move to remote learning for much of the world during the COVID-19 pandemic, while challenging to students, has also shown us the opportunities for students to connect with teachers and classrooms anywhere—and in some cases, at any time.

Develop more adaptive curricula. The increasingly internet-connected world has many trade-offs for young people in terms of lack of privacy and anonymity; the very least we can offer in return is the opportunity to get a more personalized education, one that matches a student's learning needs, skills, and potential in ways that can better prepare them for a fulfilling life and career.

Teach critical media literacy and digital literacy. The rise of misinformation and disinformation (as we'll discuss in Chapter 20: A Brighter Future for Truth and Trust) suggests that more people would benefit from skills in reading, asking critical questions, and making sense of media and institutions. A study published in PNAS in 2020 found that improving media literacy is an effective way to combat the computational propaganda that has proliferated around the world. The team used Facebook's "Tips to Spot Fake News," an article that was developed in concert with leading media literacy nonprofits and pushed to the top of newsfeeds in 2017. The five-thousand-participant study found that exposure to these simple tips (through reading and filling out a quiz to test understanding) improved people's ability to spot fake news by 26.5 percent. These results suggest that increased media literacy can improve people's ability

---

[186] https://www.teachingattherightlevel.org/

[187] The Economist, "Covid-19 creates a window for school reform in Africa," April 10, 2021. https://www.economist.com/middle-east-and-africa/2021/04/08/covid-19-creates-a-window-for-school-reform-in-africa

to separate truth from fiction online[188]—a great source of hope for us in creating a brighter future. One resource for understanding the opportunity is the 2021 Report on the Task Force on Critical Media Literacy from the National Council of Teachers of English's (NCTE).[189]

Teach young people the human skills they need for the future workplace. With so much of human work being augmented, displaced, and replaced by automation, it's important to note a few things young people should be learning now and for the foreseeable future: complements of manual skills that are harder to automate, like plumbing and other fine motor work, and the skills commonly called "soft" which are mostly mature versions of human capabilities like making decisions in context, judgment calls, nuanced management, leading with emotional intelligence, and so on.

---

[188] Proceedings of the National Academy of Sciences, "A digital media literacy intervention increases discernment between mainstream and false news in the United States and India," Andrew M. Guess, Michael Lerner, Benjamin Lyons, Jacob M. Montgomery, Brendan Nyhan, Jason Reifler, Neelanjan Sircar

Jul 2020, 117 (27) 15536-15545; DOI: 10.1073/pnas.1920498117

https://www.pnas.org/content/117/27/15536

[189] National Council of Teachers of English, 2021 Report of the Task Force on Critical Media Literacy. https://www.canva.com/design/DAERz0BpJyk/I4sPUxfrZlHLVys3QIVilQ/view?utm_content=DAERz0BpJyk&utm_campaign=designshare&utm_medium=link&utm_source=homepage_design_menu#1

Chapter 20:

A Brighter Future for Truth and Trust

IN AN ERA CHARACTERIZED BY disagreement over basic facts, where algorithmically-optimized social media platforms show us the truths we most want to see, the roles of truth and trust in ethics, in systems design, and in human experience strategy are crucial for us to understand.

We don't yet know what the consequences will be of living in a time with so many conflicting ideas of what is true. We are going to have to learn how to navigate our human understanding of trust and truth with more nuance and sophistication.

To think about how these topics intersect with the future, I'm examining questions such as: What does truth mean to us as humans; how does truth relate to belief, to science, and to law; how does truth relate to trust; and so on.

And of course:

How do divisive politics figure into our trust in institutions, and how does our sense of truth suffer from exposure to misinformation and disinformation?

And then, the big question as it relates to my work and the work of many of my clients:

What does it mean to bring machines into this dynamic? To cross-pollinate these very human concerns with data, with algorithms, with machine learning? For algorithms optimized for platform-specific engagement and retention to shape our exposure to news and opinions? We'll look more closely at a few of these areas: social media and social platforms, misinformation and disinformation.

On that last point, the twin topics of misinformation and disinformation have been a big focus this past year because of the pandemic, the US presidential election, and the widespread racial justice protests as well as the backlash against them. On seemingly every high-level topic, people had opposing views and cited opposing sources to back them up. And this went beyond the US: I had a conversation in 2019 with a journalist from the leading business magazine in Brazil, for example, about misinformation and trust, and what regulations may be needed to address them. Concerns in the US about Trump's outsized influence in shaping social media discourse mirrored those in Brazil about Bolsonaro.[190] These challenges are simultaneously local and global.

I'm not the first to think about how the notion of trust changes over time, of course. Edelman has been producing their excellent Trust Barometer every year for twenty-one years. The work I'm doing is by no means meant to be a replacement of their important research, but rather folds their findings into a holistic view on how trust and truth are fundamental to the future of humanity, and how they are important to understanding the technologies that we rely on.

Trust and business

Speaking of Edelman's Trust Barometer, one of this year's findings was that, of all the categories of institutions, business has the most public trust right now. Out of the four institutions studied—government, NGOs, media, and business—business was not only the most trusted, but also "the only institution with 61%

---

[190] Folha de S. Paolo, "É necessário fiscalizar algoritmos e regular empresas de tecnologia, diz especialista," Bruno Benevides, April 15, 2019. https://www1.folha.uol.com.br/mundo/2019/04/e-necessario-fiscalizar-algoritmos-e-regular-empresas-de-tecnologia-diz-especialista.shtml

trust globally, and the only institution seen as both ethical and competent."[191] This level of trust confers an important opportunity—and responsibility—for business, as well, when it comes to climate crisis awareness and other topics that help make the future brighter. It's a call to purpose and action; a call for transparency and for principled leadership.

Public trust in business is especially important because changes at the level of business and industry are what's needed to move the needle on climate action. That said, while individual choices aren't likely to make dramatic differences, there *is* interesting psychology wrapped up in how making sustainable choices on an individual level keeps us grounded in the mindset of what needs to change. And that offers an interesting role for businesses and brands.

While it isn't all a straight line from using a reusable coffee cup to remembering to call your elected officials, studies do connect some "positive spillover" from one desirable habit to the next. Some of the findings in this space come from a longitudinal study IKEA conducted around the consumer sustainability journey following the launch of its Live Lagom line (which means "the right amount" in Swedish). What they found was that even with a small purchase, like an LED light bulb, people tended to carry that behavior and mindset forward and began to make other related changes, such as wearing warmer clothing to reduce heating energy.

What's more, it seems that those positive spillover effects can be maximized (and negative spillover effects, whereby people reduce their subsequent commitment, can be lessened) through experience strategy and interaction design; companies and institutions can instigate desirable behaviors in their audiences and populations and nudge those behaviors ahead.

And for those businesses we define as "tech businesses" especially, not only is the public watching, but so are the eyes of history. As a crisis of democracy unfolds in the US alongside a deadly pandemic, we come face-to-face with issues of misinformation and disinformation, of content moderation and platform access, and the consequences of the algorithmic blinders we all wear as we consume social media and our preferred news outlets. Each of these issues comes tangled in its own technical details around trust and truth, but in every case, there is one central truth: The need to frame these debates and their

---

[191] Edelman, 2021 Trust Barometer. https://www.edelman.com/trust/2021-trust-barometer

outcomes not around those individuals with the largest reach but around the rights and the future of humanity at large couldn't be more urgent.

Again, given the relatively strong position of trust that companies enjoy, this seems like an excellent opportunity for brands to take on aligned actions that can help move us forward.

Some back story on truth and trust

Truth-telling is a moral imperative shared across a wide variety of cultures. Tim Bayne writes in *Thought*, "As far as we know, humans everywhere explain both their own behaviour and that of their fellow creatures by appeal to belief, desire, intention, perception, emotion, memory, and imagination."[192]

Something about the quest for truth is understood to be universal in human experience—such as in Harlan Howard's famous description of country music as "three chords and the truth."[193] But there are specific cultural overlaps in how we associate truth and trust that are worth considering as we begin to unpack this topic.

Truth and belief

Because the human mind is capable of belief, people have always believed *something*.

We arrive at an idea of what we believe to be true based on a variety of factors, but we arrive there quickly. As Steven Pinker writes in *The Sense of Style*, "More than three centuries ago, Baruch Spinoza pointed out that the human mind cannot suspend disbelief in the truth or falsity of a statement and leave it hanging in logical limbo awaiting a 'true' or 'false' tag to be hung on it."[194]

But we need more reliance on science and knowledge, and less on superstition, rumor, and dogma. Belief may be antithetical to the scientific method, to empirical knowledge, but it is not antithetical to the ways humans

---

[192] Bayne, Tim. Thought: A Very Short Introduction.
1 ed. Oxford : Oxford University Press, 2013. (Very Short Introductions).

[193] Rolling Stone, "Country Scribe Harlan Howard Dies," Andrew Dansby, March 5, 2002. https://www.rollingstone.com/music/music-news/country-scribe-harlan-howard-dies-197596/

[194] Pinker, Steven. The Sense of Style: The Thinking Person's Guide to Writing in the 21st Century. New York, New York: Viking, 2014.

understand and process the world. So we need a model that allows room for science, reasoning, and fact as well as intuition, hunches, and belief, and indeed faith, without letting the latter overpower the former when it comes to situations of public safety, public health, and so on.

Truth in science

Science doesn't define working ideas as "true," but it nonetheless relies on earnest efforts to contribute truth and only truth.

That's not to say that science is infallible. A shocking amount of scientific history is built on faulty information and false assumptions; for example, the "four humors" idea of how the body works persisted from Hippocrates for over a thousand years[195] before new ideas about germ theory began to challenge it. Tomorrow's scientific controversies, perhaps, might be string theory and other emerging ideas that are hotly contested even now.

But the scientific method is empirical, based upon evidence and what can or cannot be disproven. The field of science as a whole is characterized by adherence to this model.

During the first few months of the COVID-19 pandemic, science lost credibility because most people have too little understanding of how the scientific method works. The public took the CDC's shifting mask-wearing guidelines as a sign of incompetence, when actually it was a sign of science working as intended; the more became known, the more confident the scientific advice was about the effectiveness of wearing masks.

Science, of course, is not the same as faith; skepticism plays a healthy role in advancing scientific knowledge. But when there is broad consensus and evidence supporting an idea, it is generally productive for society to proceed as though that idea is true. The time and energy we spend debating ideas that are not controversial by scientific standards are time and energy we could be directing to solving the imminent problems we all face.

---

[195] The Western Medical Tradition: 800 BC to AD 1800. Lawrence I. Conrad, Michael Neve, Vivian Nutton, Roy Porter, Andrew Wear. 1995. https://www.cambridge.org/us/academic/subjects/history/history-medicine/western-medical-tradition-800-bc-ad-1800?format=PB&isbn=9780521475648

The relationship between truth and trust

Trust is a shortcut for not having to examine every truth. So because we can't examine truth in every single thing, we place our trust in certain kinds of authorities, leaders, and institutions to expedite things, to make those judgments on our behalf, and to guide us with the best knowledge and resources available. We accept a certain amount of trade-off here, too, whether it's in our autonomy, the facts at our disposal, etc.

But we have certain expectations in exchange: a degree of accountability, a certain amount of transparency, and trustworthiness. In the last few years, though, trust in institutions has been low, and it may be because people feel like they haven't seen that exchange play out as expected.

That would indicate that the institutions are not perceived as *trustworthy*—if trustworthiness is the idea that you are acting in accordance with the tacit assumptions made in the exchange of delegated decisions.

What about skepticism? What is the role for skepticism? Is it healthy for us to be skeptical? Is skepticism in line with Strategic Optimism?

Yes, holding ideas that purport to be truths up for examination is good. That exercise is intellectually rigorous. We more often run into trouble when we check those critical faculties at the door.

But we make a trade-off—in efficiency, and so on—for every truth we can't accept at face value. If we closely examine every single thought shared, every single idea, we will find ourselves stuck and stagnant.

So if we work our way back up through this thought process, trustworthiness is critical to the proper functioning of society, and trust is only maintained when institutions adhere to the social contract of acting in accordance with accountability to the truth.

Is objectivity possible?

Is objectivity possible? Is it desirable? Is it necessary for Strategic Optimism to work?

Media critic Jay Rosen coined the term "The View from Nowhere" in 2003 to describe, as he puts it, "a bid for trust that advertises the viewlessness of the news producer." Yet in times of increasing distortion of facts, that attempt at fairness can give weight to "alternative facts" and theories that have no basis in credible science or observable phenomena. Sometimes we just have to call falsehoods out.

There's a difference between legitimate disagreement and what is popularly known as "both-sides-ism." Disagreement is about respecting the nuances and allowing for multiple people to hold conflicting opinions and beliefs—whereas both-sides-ism demands that whenever one view is expressed, people must grant equal weight to whatever is the logical opposite of that view, no matter its own inherent logic or lack of basis in reality.

Consider that some views are informed by well-researched facts, by a consensus of experts, and by credible media outlets. One such view is that the earth is round. This would seem hardly controversial, except that for any view, inevitably there will be people who don't like it—people who decide that it's wrong, that it's inconvenient, that it infringes on their personal sense of fairness. A counter-perspective emerges: Flat Earthers. And an entire ecosystem of media outlets develops to support this alternative—and factually incorrect— perspective. (Perhaps in this case I should give that word sarcasm italics: *perspective*.)

And the cultural ideal of fairness and equality, the View from Nowhere, dictates that we give equal time and equal weight to "both sides." (*Both sides*.)

We will not be able to advance past this "post-truth" limbo until we adopt the mindset that while there is indeed truth on multiple sides in many cases, truth is not drawn from the dueling both-sides-ism that shows up in politics, media, and cultural discourse. A credible idea does not imply a credible opposite. Differing views can offer nuance; polarized views shut down discourse.

So what does all this mean for Strategic Optimism? It demonstrates the need to surround ourselves with as much objective data as we can, to see beyond our biases, to allow informed reason to influence our decision-making, and to resist cutting ourselves off from reality. And then to commit to the direction that serves humanity best.

Machines, truth, and trust

When it comes to understanding the role machines play and will increasingly play in our relationship to truth and trust, we have a lot to unpack. After all, machines "believe" what they're told. Machines can come to faulty "truths" based on faulty data, limited data, misleading data, or poorly structured data.

Humans, on the other hand—well, we can just be fooled by tapping into our social instincts.

One problem is that we—humans who are only now getting used to the phenomenon of living in the internet ether—often suspend the senses we have in the natural world when we interact online. We don't have the same "spidey-senses" of intuition that tell us when something isn't quite right. On the other hand, that would seem to suggest we're bringing less biased baggage into our online interactions, but experience so far doesn't necessarily bear that out.

In any case, we don't necessarily see the problems with memes, games, and other interactions that either mine us for data that can be used at scale in manipulative ways, or that sow misinformation in the guise of entertainment.

Social platforms, algorithms, filter bubbles, and false news

In 1710 the satirist Jonathan Swift wrote: "Falsehood flies, and truth comes limping after it, so that when men come to be undeceived, it is too late; the jest is over, and the tale hath had its effect."[196] He didn't even need social media to prove it, but prove it social media has.

A study by three MIT scholars in 2018 found that false news spreads substantially faster on Twitter than real news does: "False news stories are 70 percent more likely to be retweeted than true stories are. It also takes true stories

---

[196] Jonathan Swift (1667-1745) in The Examiner, "The Art of Political Lying" November 9, 1710.

about six times as long to reach 1,500 people as it does for false stories to reach the same number of people."[197]

Fake news and misinformation lead to algorithmic polarization—essentially what Eli Pariser called "filter bubbles" in 2011 but which have grown considerably in scale and sophistication since then. Because they often rely heavily on memes to make fast impressions as people scroll (whether to turn the discourse in favor of their own views or to sow chaos), they tend to be extreme and reductionist, all but eliminating nuance and areas of common interest. This leads to more frequent uses of engagement triggers, particularly the "anger" reaction emoji on Facebook, which can factor in to the algorithms that determine how content gets weighted and shown to which audiences. This becomes an accelerating cycle of manufactured outrage. But outrage is a highly-engaged emotion, so it creates tension for the platform—meaning the platforms are not incentivized to reduce this cycle.

This even has public health consequences, as we'll examine in The misinformation pandemic.

Twitter did roll out a feature in late 2020 that asks users retweeting an article if they want to read the article first. Many people are sure to have found the feature patronizing, but a 2016 tongue-in-cheek experiment by the satirical website The Science Post had already demonstrated the underlying problem: entitled "70% of Facebook users only read the headline of science stories before commenting,"[198] the "article" racked up almost 130,000 shares—even though it's almost entirely comprised of "lorem ipsum" filler text.

On the more serious side of social media research, computer scientists at Columbia University and Microsoft found, also in 2016, that 59 percent of shared links posted on Twitter are never clicked.[199] When scientists and satirists are making the same points, it might be a good idea to pay attention.

---

[197] MIT News Office, "Study: On Twitter, false news travels faster than true stories," Peter Dizikes, March 8, 2018. https://news.mit.edu/2018/study-twitter-false-news-travels-faster-true-stories-0308

[198] The Science Post, "Study: 70% of Facebook users only read the headline of science stories before commenting," March 5, 2018. http://thesciencepost.com/study-70-of-facebook-commenters-only-read-the-headline/

[199] Maksym Gabielkov, Arthi Ramachandran, Augustin Chaintreau, Arnaud Legout. "Social Clicks: What and Who Gets Read on Twitter?". ACM SIGMETRICS / IFIP Performance 2016, Jun 2016, Antibes Juan-les-Pins, France. hal-01281190
https://hal.inria.fr/hal-01281190/document

So this kind of "do you want to read the article first" prompt and other interactions encouraging us to slow down and consider what we share may well be a sensible experiment in presenting an opportunity for a cognitive pause in the outrage cycle. Wherever possible, we should be looking for opportunities to break that outrage cycle outright and foster healthier, more trustworthy interactions online.

Blockchain: attempting to codify what is trustworthy

In an entirely different facet of the relationship of machines and trust, there is the problem of validation and certification. Knowing that a transaction is what it claims to be, that a person is who they claim to be, that a vote is a vote, that money is money, and so on—all of these are in the domain of digital trust that many blockchain solutions seek in some way to address.

Perhaps all emerging technologies attract their devoted fans, but it seems none in my lifetime has attracted such devoted fans as blockchain and cryptocurrencies. When it comes to the issue of trust and transparency, that is indeed where blockchain shines: The fundamentals of the technology mean that everyone has the same records, and committing fraud is very difficult if not impossible.

Does that mean we can look to blockchain for opportunities to validate and verify what is confirmed to be true? Certainly there are moves in this direction; contracts have been a favorite use case for blockchain. In one of the most widely cited examples among blockchain enthusiasts, Estonia's entire digitized government and decentralized services also rely heavily on a blockchain technology built within the country[200], and by all accounts it has meant incredible simplification for its citizens. They can vote online and even change their vote within the allocated period with no worries of fraud; they can file their taxes quickly; hospitals can access patients' medical records easily; and so on.[201]

---

[200] e-estonia, "Security and safety," https://e-estonia.com/solutions/security-and-safety/

[201] The Conversation, "Estonia is a 'digital republic' – what that means and why it may be everyone's future," Imtiaz Khan, Ali Shahaab, October 7, 2020. https://theconversation.com/estonia-is-a-digital-republic-what-that-means-and-why-it-may-be-everyones-future-145485

Another great example in line with the brighter future is that of humanitarian funding. Because humanitarian efforts and the government organizations and NGOs that engage in them are scrutinized[202] as not being adequately transparent or accountable and are often riddled with corruption[203], humanitarian aid accountability has been a big opportunity space.

A UK-based charity, Positive Women, used Disberse[204], a distribution platform for aid funding, to successfully reduce its transfer fees and trace the flow of funds to a project in Swaziland. More recently, Disberse began a partnership with the Start Network, made up of fifty agencies across five continents, to develop blockchain in the area of humanitarian financing. This partnership aimed to make funding more efficient and effective and to increase transparency, which drives accountability to both taxpayers and those affected by crises.

Though Disberse's pilot program did make a lot of progress toward building a new type of financial institution for aid, they weren't able to achieve their end goals due to COVID-19. But they wanted to encourage anybody who's hoping to start their own moonshot project, so they converted their website into a learning hub where they share their journey and the lessons learned on the way.[205]

On the other hand, we can't overlook the ecological cost of blockchain and the energy redundancy needed to maintain up-to-date ledgers on distributed machines. Bitcoin, the best-known cryptocurrency based on blockchain technology, is said to require so much energy in the mining process that it consumes more than several countries combined, including Kazakhstan and the Netherlands, according to a 2021 UN report.[206] That report adds:

---

[202] Brookings, "How better aid transparency will help tackle global development challenges," George Ingram, June 21, 2018. https://www.brookings.edu/blog/up-front/2018/06/21/how-better-aid-transparency-will-help-tackle-global-development-challenges/

[203] The Guardian, "Big aid donors failing to lift the lid on how they spend their cash," Clár Ní Chonghaile, April 13, 2016. https://www.theguardian.com/global-development/2016/apr/13/big-aid-donors-failing-spend-cash-campaign-transparency

[204] https://www.disberse.com/

[205] https://startnetwork.org/news-and-blogs/blockchain-experiment-humanitarian-aid

[206] https://news.un.org/en/story/2021/06/1094362

"Another problem is the amount of energy needed for each transaction, which is enormous in comparison to traditional credit cards: for example, each Mastercard transaction is estimated to use just 0.0006 kWh (kilowatt hours), whilst every Bitcoin transaction consumes 980 kWh, enough to power an average Canadian home for more than three weeks, according to some commentators."

In spite of all this, though, the technology has its advantages, and those play right back into trust: transparency and accountability are the key strengths of blockchain and cryptocurrencies.

The misinformation pandemic

The battle with COVID-19 has been made more complicated by our also having to deal with another pandemic: misinformation—spread intentionally, accidentally, sensationally, and routinely.

Even disinformation.

In May 2020, the "Plandemic" video went viral. Even though multiple platforms moved quickly to limit or remove it, the video was viewed more than eight million times.

Casey Newton, writing for The Verge, reported[207] that a twenty-six-minute clip of "Plandemic"—the cut that became the most viewed and most famous—was uploaded to YouTube on May 4 and removed May 6, and in that time, it generated 7.1 million views.

> "In the 26-minute video, the woman asserted how Dr. Fauci, the director of the National Institute of Allergy and Infectious Diseases and a leading voice on the coronavirus, had buried her research about how vaccines can damage people's immune systems. It is those weakened immune systems, she declared, that have made people susceptible to illnesses like Covid-19.
>
> "The video, a scene from a longer dubious documentary called 'Plandemic,' was quickly seized upon by anti-vaccinators, the conspiracy group QAnon and activists from the Reopen America movement, generating more than eight

---

[207] The Verge, "How the 'Plandemic' video hoax went viral," Casey Newton, May 12, 2020. https://www.theverge.com/2020/5/12/21254184/how-plandemic-went-viral-facebook-youtube

million views. And it has turned the woman—Dr. Judy Mikovits, 62, a discredited scientist—into a new star of virus disinformation."

— Davey Alba in the New York Times[208]

As we discussed in the last section, fake news and misinformation are huge problems for platforms themselves where the content is hosted, since that can erode trust over time. But they are bigger problems for the people who consume the content—and even more, for the people affected by the people who consume the content.

That means that fake news is a human problem at scale. And problems for people at scale are arguably problems where regulation is worth exploring. Left to their own management, the platforms may not act aggressively enough.

Twitter, for example, in May of 2020 marked then-President Trump's tweets claiming voting by mail would be fraudulent as having been fact-checked, which was a historic move made possible by a policy they instituted mainly thinking about COVID-19 misinformation[209]. But many previous tweets from the former president were misleading and actively promoted violent attitudes toward Americans. None of those were flagged or removed.

What's more, the broader category of computational propaganda involves actors and motives across national boundaries, and the result is confusion and chaos for citizens, consumers, and humans in all roles of life.

In December 2016, Garry Kasparov tweeted:

"The point of modern propaganda isn't only to misinform or push an agenda. It is to exhaust your critical thinking, to annihilate truth."

---

[208] The New York Times, "Virus Conspiracists Elevate a New Champion," Davey Alba, May 9, 2020. https://www.nytimes.com/2020/05/09/technology/plandemic-judy-mikovitz-coronavirus-disinformation.html

[209] Reuters, "Twitter fact-checks Trump tweet for the first time," Katie Paul, Elizabeth Culliford, May 26, 2020. https://www.reuters.com/article/us-twitter-trump/twitter-fact-checks-trump-tweet-for-the-first-time-idUSKBN232389

Will it be possible to develop regulation that can address protections for citizens even from the highest-ranking elected officials? That's going to be a challenge, but it's one researchers are already studying and making recommendations around. They're complex enough to fill entire books, but for our purposes, as leaders, we have to do our best in the context of our own environments to recognize the problematic patterns, cast our thinking ahead, and act on behalf of future citizens.

Conspiracy theories and the quest for meaning

The human quest for meaning could well be why we have such a problem with conspiracy theories. Because people are constantly searching for meaning and patterns, we'll see them everywhere and anywhere. But without reliable access to reliable information, with public education having been cut over the past decades, and with libraries losing funding, and all of the sources we rely on for an informed electorate, we're seeing that it's down to people taking the time to educate themselves. When you combine that dynamic with a mesh of social platforms that monetize engagement, it's inevitable that they would seek to promote the most engaging emotions, including outrage.

So outrageous content makes rapid-fire rounds on these platforms. Renee DiResta has called this phenomenon on social media "asymmetry of passion":

"On many issues, the most active social media voices are the conspiracist fringe. The majority of people know that vaccines don't cause autism, and that 9/11 was not an inside job. They don't dedicate hours to creating content or tweeting to reinforce the obvious. But passionate truthers and extremists produce copious

---

[210] https://twitter.com/kasparov63/status/808750564284702720

amounts of content in their commitment to 'wake up the sheeple.'" [211]

But this perhaps gives us a dimensional way to look at how to combat conspiracy theories and misinformation; we need to do a better job of making meaningful patterns more accessible. So much of the way forward into the brighter future comes back to an emphasis on meaning.

---

[211] "Social Network Algorithms Are Distorting Reality By Boosting Conspiracy Theories, Fast Company," Renee DiResta, May 11, 2016. https://www.fastcompany.com/3059742/social-network-algorithms-are-distorting-reality-by-boosting-conspiracy-theories

Towards a brighter future for truth and trust

The forces pulling society into fractured understandings of truth and whom to trust may not be reconcilable anytime soon. But society must still function, meaning we each need to be able to navigate a complicated media and cultural landscape and understand what is credible and what deserves our suspicion.

How can we combat mistrust, fakery, and fraud?

It may seem counterintuitive, but machines may be the best tool in staving off machine-assisted fakery. AI may be best poised to detect manipulative AI. If so, it will be a battle of speed between manipulative deepfakes and the machine intelligence to recognize and flag them as they appear in social media and elsewhere.

One area of opportunity amid increasing digital identity complexity and cybersecurity threats is to identify digital solutions to combat ID theft and fraud.

Take the situation in Brazil, for example. In 2020, Brazil implemented the General Law for the Protection of Personal Data. Soon after that, a security breach at the Ministry of Health exposed the data of more than 243 million Brazilians. (Interestingly, that number is higher than the country's total population because the breach included the data of deceased people.) Moreover, Brazil accounted for 45.4 percent of global cases of credit card fraud in 2020[212], and a little less than a third of Brazilian adults are unbanked.[213] Brazil's citizens are issued an array of official documents from various decentralized and

---

[212] The Rio Times, "Brazil 'Champion' in Card Fraud, With 45.4% of Global Cases – Report," Oliver Mason, February 1, 2021. https://riotimesonline.com/brazil-news/brazil/brazil-champion-in-card-fraud-with-45-4-of-global-cases/

[213] The World Bank Group, "The Global Findex Database 2017: Chapter 2: The unbanked," https://globalfindex.worldbank.org/sites/globalfindex/files/chapters/2017%20Findex%20full%20report_chapter2.pdf

complex levels of government, yet Brazil is also highly digitized, ranking fifth in a 2019 ranking of countries with the highest number of internet users.[214]

Because of these factors, startups that provide digital identification platforms have skyrocketed in popularity since 2016. One such company is idwall, which provides a suite of data and identity validation and risk analysis products and, for the consumer market, a "MeuID" app that is aimed at users who want to change the way they identify themselves and share their data. Idwall uses regtech to keep up with regulation changes, provide real-time fraud detection, and verify identities.[215]

What do we need to hold technology companies accountable for?

Social media platforms, search engines, and other content providers and hosts are in an ongoing debate about human intervention versus machine recognition of suspect patterns, as well as about removal and censorship versus free speech.

Part of the challenge is a linguistic one. The terminology we use to describe products like Facebook and Twitter shapes the cognitive space we can debate them in—and to some extent the laws that apply to them. They aren't exactly "publishers" since they're not directly creating the content people subscribe to; nor are they exactly "platforms," which would suggest a level of neutrality and detachment from what happens on them. The algorithmic optimization of content users are exposed to to enhance their engagement gives the lie to any such neutrality. And as tech ethicist David Ryan Polgar points out, calling them "public squares" suggests a government-run resource in the public interest, which then shouldn't be run by a private company.[216] Besides, it offers them a veneer of quasi-governmental legitimacy that isn't right either. (David suggests

---

[214] Forbes, "Understanding The Significance Of Digital Identification Problems In Latin America," Lincoln Ando, June 2, 2021. https://www.forbes.com/sites/forbestechcouncil/2021/06/02/understanding-the-significance-of-digital-identification-problems-in-latin-america/?sh=17246790525f

[215] Techcrunch, "Brazil's idwall raises $38M for identity validation platform," Mary Ann Azevedo, June 1, 2021. https://techcrunch.com/2021/06/01/brazils-idwall-raises-38m-for-identity-validation-platform/

[216] Built In, "Social Media Isn't a Platform. So What Is It?," David Ryan Polgar, July 15, 2021. https://builtin.com/consumer-tech/social-media-platform

"springboard.") Whatever we call them, it matters that we are clear about what they do and how they function in order to hold them accountable in the right way.

Meanwhile, we can hold the political process itself accountable for clarity and transparency. Data-enabled platforms that collect information about candidates for voters and about politicians for constituents can enhance adherence to truth in politics.

What can we do for ourselves?

We have to understand, first of all, as much as possible how and where our data is being collected, then try to recognize manipulative schemes for what they are. Memes and games that ask for specific kinds of participation are some of the easiest traps to avoid.

It's a good reality check for us to proceed with a simultaneous understanding that there is misinformation and disinformation out there but that what you see in your feeds is tailored to you so you can trust it. That's a weird duality for the human experience. We can and must be just skeptical enough to question the validity of the stories we hear before we amplify them.

We can manage our data footprint more actively. That means unsubscribing from mailing lists you don't care about, deleting accounts on platforms you don't use anymore and don't need access to, unfollowing pages on Facebook you aren't invested in, and so on. (Or get off of Facebook altogether. That's your call.)

But one thing we do want to do is stay human in our use of technology. So within the circles that feel comfortable to you, stay as transparent as you feel it is safe and relevant to do, and strive for authenticity.

Chapter 21:

A Brighter Future for How And What We Eat

PRESERVING HUMAN LIFE ON THIS planet is going to require lightening our footprint, and one of the most profound ways we can do that collectively is through a greater emphasis on sustainable eating and regenerative agriculture.

Four major food crops—wheat, corn, rice, soy—that together provide two-thirds of human caloric intake, are likely to be significantly reduced by rising temperatures by 2050, yet the demand for food will nearly double to feed the nine billion people on the planet by that time[217].

At the same time, 20–30 percent of animal and plant species are facing extinction because temperatures are changing too fast for them to be able to

---

[217] PNAS, "Temperature increase reduces global yields," Chuang Zhao, Bing Liu, Shilong Piao, Xuhui Wang, David B. Lobell, Yao Huang, Mengtian Huang, Yitong Yao, Simona Bassu, Philippe Ciais, Jean-Louis Durand, Joshua Elliott, Frank Ewert, Ivan A. Janssens, Tao Li, Erda Lin, Qiang Liu, Pierre Martre, Christoph Müller, Shushi Peng, Josep Peñuelas, Alex C. Ruane, Daniel Wallach, Tao Wang, Donghai Wu, Zhuo Liu, Yan Zhu, Zaichun Zhu, Senthold Asseng, Proceedings of the National Academy of Sciences Aug 2017, 114 (35) 9326-9331; DOI: 10.1073/pnas.1701762114

adapt. As a vivid example of this kind of rapid change, animals whose fur turns white in the winter to help them camouflage in the snow, such as white-tailed jackrabbits and Arctic foxes, are now facing winters with far less snow, and now their white fur leaves them far more vulnerable in a brown landscape.[218]

As a result of heat waves and record high temperatures in Northern California in the summer of 2021, officials forecasted that all the juvenile chinook salmon in the Sacramento River could die off.[219] One could not overstate the impact that could have, not only on our direct human food supply but also on animal populations that depend on salmon as a food source—which indirectly affects our own food supply because of the chain of impact.

The bright future of food has the opportunity to be one of mindfulness and connectedness to one another, of considering our decisions in terms of their impact on the planet and on human and nonhuman life. Like the recurring theme it is, collective action is a relevant construct here too. We have the opportunity to think small, local, and connected, but at scale: community gardens, small-scale agriculture, farm-to-table food, restaurants growing their own herbs and other produce on rooftop gardens—these are all trends that have been growing. (Sorry, the pun couldn't be avoided.)

Remember: Everything is connected. While it may be easy to dismiss a story about the climate impact on an animal you don't eat, we are considering the impact that changes like these will ultimately have on the overall ecosystem. The impact from a change like this to how your community eats is only a few falling dominos away. And we must consider the broader pattern of change and what it requires of us.

What we eat impacts the future too

What can we do as individuals? We can start by beginning to adopt a primarily plant-based diet. Many experts agree that plant-based diets will help reduce the burden of agriculture. For example, for every one hundred calories

---

[218] https://www.carbonbrief.org/animals-with-white-winter-camouflage-could-struggle-to-adapt-to-climate-change
7/18/21, 2:45 PM

[219] CNN, "Extreme heat could kill nearly all young salmon in the Sacramento River, officials say," Alexandra Meeks, July 14, 2021. https://www.cnn.com/2021/07/14/weather/extreme-heat-salmon-sacramento-river/index.html

fed to a farm animal, we only receive forty calories back.[220] Conversely, plant-based diets could add up to 49 percent more food to the global food supply without expanding croplands.[221] One study states that if we replaced all meat and dairy products with plant-based food, land use could be reduced by 50 percent.[222]

A 2019 study from researchers at Oxford and published in the journal *Science* even found that not eating dairy and meat products can reduce an individual's carbon footprint by up to 73 percent.[223]

Our overly commercialized approach to agriculture and livestock has been part of a growing problem, and we can see its effects on humans, too, directly through their workplaces. Meatpacking was one of the most dangerous industries for human workers during the COVID-19 pandemic. The thousands of COVID-19 cases in facilities like Tyson's exposed some of the labor conditions many people have been historically able to ignore.

The effects of animal agriculture—specifically cattle ranching—is the biggest cause of deforestation in the Amazon rainforest.[224] Raising cattle for meat consumption is going to be increasingly unsustainable.

I've been vegetarian since 1995 and vegan since 1998, so I will admit to some bias here, but a wide array of research continually confirms that diets prioritizing plants and locally-sourced food can make more efficient use of natural resources and use agricultural land more efficiently.

That said, the emphasis on *plants*—in other words, vegetables and legumes —is key; studies do show that while vegan diets are generally agreed to be the best for the planet in theory, in practice many people end up swapping in

---

[220] Environmental Research Letters, "Redefining agricultural yields: from tonnes to people nourished per hectare" Emily S Cassidy et al 2013 Environ. Res. Lett. 8 (2013) 034015 https://iopscience.iop.org/article/10.1088/1748-9326/8/3/034015/pdf
[221] Environmental Research Letters, "Diet change—a solution to reduce water use?" M Jalava et al, 2014 Environ. Res. Lett. 9 074016 https://iopscience.iop.org/article/10.1088/1748-9326/9/7/074016/meta
[222] Pimentel, D.; Pimentel, M. Sustainability of meat-based and plant-based diets and the environment. Am. J. Clin. Nutr. 2003, 78, 660–663.
[223] Science, "Reducing food's environmental impacts through producers and consumers," J. Poore, T. Nemecek, 01 Jun 2018 : 987-992
[224] The World Bank, World Bank Working Paper No. 22, "Causes of Deforestation of the Brazilian Amazon," p.59 https://documents1.worldbank.org/curated/en/758171468768828889/pdf/277150PAPER0wbwp0no1022.pdf

processed meat and dairy substitutes, which causes their overall greenhouse gas emissions (GHGEs) to be higher than they could or should be. (They're clearly counting my occasional splurges on vegan cheeseburgers and fries.)

Still, as an overall direction, plant-based vegan diets result in the lowest level of GHG emissions.

One review of the academic literature around dietary impacts states:

"Nonetheless, one study estimates that a complete switch to a vegan diet could result in reductions of 17% for CO2, 21% for NO2 and 24% for CH4. Among the three diets, the vegan diet makes the lightest demands on the global water supply, requiring 14.4% less freshwater and 20.8% less ground water than the omnivorous diet."[225]

While we're talking about water usage, we can also learn that reducing animal-based consumption could save up to 50 percent of fresh water usage a year. Because, for example, one pound of beef requires between two and five thousand gallons to produce, while one pound of tofu requires only 302 gallons.[226]

Here are some more striking comparisons: Eating a plant-based diet has three times more positive impact than washing your clothes in cold water, four times more positive impact than hang-drying clothes or recycling, and eight times more positive impact than upgrading light bulbs.[227]

And fear not! It doesn't have to be a complicated, miserable, or expensive switch. A 2019 comparative review of research on veganism, vegetarianism, and

[225] Chai, Bingli C., Johannes R. van der Voort, Kristina Grofelnik, Helga G. Eliasdottir, Ines Klöss, and Federico J.A. Perez-Cueto 2019. "Which Diet Has the Least Environmental Impact on Our Planet? A Systematic Review of Vegan, Vegetarian and Omnivorous Diets" Sustainability 11, no. 15: 4110. https://doi.org/10.3390/su11154110

[226] Environmental Research Letters, "Diet change—a solution to reduce water use?" M Jalava et al, 2014 Environ. Res. Lett. 9 074016 https://iopscience.iop.org/article/10.1088/1748-9326/9/7/074016/meta

[227] Environmental Research Letters, "The climate mitigation gap: education and government recommendations miss the most effective individual actions Seth Wynes and Kimberly A Nicholas, 2017 Environ. Res. Lett. 12 074024 https://iopscience.iop.org/article/10.1088/1748-9326/aa7541

omnivore diets published in *Sustainability* points out that simply eating beans instead of beef offers substantial benefits[228] for you *and* the planet:

> "Consuming legumes for protein instead of meat has a beneficial environmental impact, and it is also a lot cheaper[229]. A life cycle assessment analysis suggests that, if beans were substituted for beef, then 692,918 km2 of US cropland could be freed up for other uses and GHGEs from this land would decrease by 74%[230]."

So while my occasional vegan cheeseburger and fries aren't really all that good for either me or the planet, as long as they're the exception and the emphasis is on plants, a vegan diet is going to be the best choice most of us could make for the planet.

Innovations in food

Alongside the emphasis on reducing our dietary footprint through a focus on substituting plants for animals, there is another parallel future of food, and it's actually taking place in laboratories: the revolution in food technologies and innovations.

If you read the section above and thought, "But I could never give up the taste of beef," you're exactly the consumer innovators have in mind with the efforts to grow meat in labs. Lab-grown meat or simulated meat will become a useful substitute or transition food for people who are struggling to give up the livestock from their plates.

But in addition to all of this futuristic-sounding food, everyday agriculture is becoming more digitally transformed too.

---

[228] Chai, Bingli C., Johannes R. van der Voort, Kristina Grofelnik, Helga G. Eliasdottir, Ines Klöss, and Federico J.A. Perez-Cueto 2019. "Which Diet Has the Least Environmental Impact on Our Planet? A Systematic Review of Vegan, Vegetarian and Omnivorous Diets" Sustainability 11, no. 15: 4110. https://doi.org/10.3390/su11154110

[229] Tyszler, M.; Kramer, G.F.H.; Blonk, H. Just eating healthier is not enough: Studying the environmental impact of different diet scenarios for the Netherlands by Linear Programming. Int. J. Life Cycle Assess. 2016, 21, 701–709.

[230] Harwatt, H.; Sabaté, J.; Eshel, G.; Soret, S.; Ripple, W. Substituting beans for beef as a contribution toward US climate change targets. Clim. Chang. 2017, 143, 261–270.

Exponential technologies stand to make nutritious food more available to more people, and there is a rise in precision farming. Apps like OneSoil[231] use a combination of satellite imaging and AI to monitor and optimize crops and provide useful insights to farmers.

And if all of this is done in conjunction with what Indigenous people have traditionally done and what has been historically understood about techniques like crop rotation, soil replenishment, etc.—we stand a chance at brightening the future of food.

A whole raft of interconnected food scarcity and quality issues poses challenges and opportunities for communities to address them as a whole. Problems such as food access and hunger, food supply chains, food deserts, and food waste tend not to be isolated issues. Local and community-based organizations thinking holistically and collectively can address them as part of a process that brightens the future of food, particularly for people with the least access to quality food.

Take for example the Atlanta Metro Area's Food Well Alliance, a collaborative network of growers, community and city leaders all working together to build thriving community gardens and urban farms. The organization also used the COVID-19 pandemic as an opportunity to reassert the case for locally-grown food as the safest, healthiest food available to us, positioning it as immune-boosting, easiest to access when under lockdown orders/quarantine etc.[232]

Food is too fundamental to human thriving for us not to take a more holistic look at how we can improve its cultivation, distribution, sustainability, and sharing.

---

[231] https://onesoil.ai/en/
[232] https://www.foodwellalliance.org/

Chapter 22:

A Brighter Future for Energy

DURING THE EARLY PART OF the 2020s, the vision for energy is shaped by two dates: 2030 and 2050. Those are the milestone years by which most of the world's governments and institutions have recognized significant progress needs to be made, in alignment with what climate science tells us about the effects of average warming.

Some of what's possible in the near future is already underway in small experiments. AI and other emerging tech could have tremendous impact on energy and climate advances. Wind and solar energy, for example, can be made substantially more efficient with AI. To make the most of renewable energy sources, even with the help of AI, we have to do better with battery storage, but that's starting to happen.

The bigger, bolder, brighter vision for the future for energy has less to do with technology per se, although tech can certainly play a key role in supporting it:

We need a massive shift in *thinking* to move our underlying decision frameworks from a misguided sense of infinite resources and finite opportunity to a more strategic and hopeful picture of finite resources and infinite opportunity. That shift is possible through an emphasis on circular economies and resource sustainability. And the gains we make from these sustainability advances—in efficiency, in sophistication, in profit—must be channeled back into further restoration and renewal. A deeply regenerative approach is the only way to think that gets us to the brighter future we're trying to create.

To do this holistically we will need to get creative with economic incentives, whether that involves offsets, green energy credits, or new programs at local, state, or national levels.

One of the more aggressive and comprehensive plans for rethinking energy policy came from the European Union in summer 2021, just as Germany and Belgium reeled from killer floods that were likely exacerbated by the climate crisis.[233] The EU announced its "Fit for 55" plans, "a set of inter-connected proposals, which all drive toward the same goal of ensuring a fair, competitive and green transition by 2030 and beyond."[234]

It's an approach that is systemic, recognizing the interconnectedness of a wide variety of policy areas and economic sectors: energy, transportation, buildings, land use, and forestry.

While the commission had set a goal in 2018 of 32 percent green energy sources, the new plan calls for 40 percent renewables in the mix by 2030. That means clean energy plans like wind farms will likely accelerate; higher targets for efficiency measures are expected to be part of this program too.[235]

All in all, we need both ambitious plans *and* the will to achieve them.

---

[233] https://www.economist.com/europe/2021/07/16/devastating-floods-in-germany-warn-europe-of-the-dangers-of-warming

[234] European Commission, "'Fit for 55': delivering the EU's 2030 Climate Target on the way to climate neutrality," https://ec.europa.eu/info/sites/default/files/chapeau_communication.pdf

[235] The Economist "The Climate Issue" email, July 12th 2021

PART SIX:

Tools for a Brighter Future Overall

Before we go, here are a few additional lists and ideas to help you lead us forward with Strategic Optimism, along with some reminders about the tools we have discussed for easy reference.

Chapter 23:

Leading with optimism

YOU ARE A LEADER. WE know this because otherwise you wouldn't be reading this book. So having come all this way, and now empowered with the tools of Strategic Optimism, how will you infuse them into your leadership and practices? How can you make the shift toward Strategic Optimism in your own leadership style?

Look for leading indicators, even if they're qualitative

I look for leading indicators—even qualitative ones, such as how well my message seems to be resonating, in addition to pragmatic indicators like cash flow and profit. I often think of these leading indicators as optimistic measures, because while they're not set in stone, they often suggest an optimistic outcome that motivates me and my teams to excel.

Have teams talk about "best-case scenario" planning

Many teams use some kind of worst-case scenario planning to deal with unknowns, but both of these approaches together present the fullest picture of the range of possibilities. If you're not planning for the best case, you may miss opportunities to scale when a market alignment hits.

Focus on organizational purpose

From a speaking and consulting practice standpoint, when I work with executives and other leaders around digital transformation and emerging tech strategy, a lot of our work begins with organizational purpose. The holistic view of purpose is a powerful one, bringing values, priorities, and resources into alignment toward objectives that are both optimistic and strategic.

Emphasize value rather than profit

Business isn't *only* about making money. Arguably a corporation is, by nature; but within a company, humans are the ones doing the work (for now), and by *our* nature we generally need more than money to drive us to do our best work. So for us, let's prioritize creating something of value and building out that value through interaction with people. (There's plenty of money to be made in focusing on value, so this emphasis is not at odds with traditional business direction; it's just a more human-centric way of arriving there.) My belief is that there is a subculture in business of the people who recognize the opportunity to create value. These people are interested in being rewarded for their work and their ideas, but they're also interested in building something great.

Make the connection between purpose and leading with optimism

It is an optimistic thing to say I am putting resources together to solve this problem I have identified, and I am saying out loud that I am doing so, because I want my friends and my frenemies to know what I am up to. I want them to be able to recognize opportunities in the world that relate to my purpose.

But the real reason for articulating purpose is more internal than that; it allows you to test your own commitment every day, in small ways that could otherwise derail you. If you know you're trying to solve human problem X and you get the opportunity to partner with a company focused on Y, you need a very clear way to analyze and shape the terms of that partnership and how you want it to unfold.

Develop a meaningful metrics model

This model could allow leaders to see years ahead beyond revenue growth and also develop team morale, market adaptability, better aligned priorities, and more sustainable practices. Doing this requires asking what is not only useful but also meaningful to measure across the business.

Cultivate people to be their best at work

Encourage people to bring their own optimism to their work, to seek better results from themselves and from the company, and to contribute their best ideas.

Align with human outcomes when you don't know where to start

The best objectives you can have, in business or any endeavor, are those which are aligned with human outcomes: They are true to your strategic purpose, and they line up with the goals people outside of the organization have when they interact with you.

When in doubt, align with the SDGs. Make sure justice and equity are woven into every decision you make, every design you create, every plan you oversee.

Envision the better world you want to live in, and work to build it

Business too often absolves itself of its role in building culture and society, but many if not most of our everyday experiences are driven by business. If we as people want to live in the better world we hope is possible, we have to embrace how we can adapt the decisions we make in our workplaces. An optimistic view of the future is one that believes the world can be improved and that our actions can improve it.

Chapter 24:

What to take forward

THE BRIGHT FUTURE IS GOING to require some contribution from all of us: each of us doing our part, in proportion. In particular, if you are leading within the following areas, here are some summaries and considerations for the future.

For companies: adapt to a bright future

What you may notice is that I'm saying: Businesses need new skills too.

Which means: Hire and promote people who can adapt.

Organizations need adaptability almost more than anything right now, but they also need people with the creative vision to spot undeveloped and adaptable talent and cultivate it.

Encourage good judgment up and down and across the organization.

And for all our sakes, hire and promote people who can see the humanity in data, who make empathetic decisions about the humans who will be using technologies.

For cities and places: focus on a new understanding of livability

Focus on what the future of livability in your city will look like. Realistically, are you facing the prospect of clean water shortages, rising sea levels, hurricane threats, or other recurring natural disasters? Addressing those pragmatic issues —hopefully in a creative, locally-relevant way that offers job opportunities, strategic partnerships, development incentives, and more—must be a focus in protecting human well-being as well as the collective investments people have made in the city.

For regulators: secure our public future

Companies can do plenty of work within the free market; for example, they can make their offering more appealing by aligning with human interests and making it clear why that alignment benefits people.

Government's ongoing challenge in policy and regulation around innovation will be to anticipate the exact mechanics of novel systems and their impact.

But governments do have a right and responsibility to step in and provide teeth to the insurance that human data is treated well.

Where misinformation, false news, and social content platforms are concerned, regulators must recognize the problematic patterns, get the best expert input they can from those who work in the public's interest, cast their thinking ahead, and act on behalf of future citizens.

For individuals: cultivate human skills for the next era

Finally, there's the responsibility we each have as individuals to ourselves. We need to learn new skills.

You know what skills we need to prepare ourselves for jobs we don't even know exist yet? What futuristic, cutting-edge skills we need?

Good judgment, cooperation, delegation, organization, project management —all those "soft skills," which is another way of saying human skills.

But there are some other things too.

We need to develop digital literacy, media literacy, and awareness of algorithmic systems.

We need to get curious, for example, about why we see the content we see in our social media and our search results.

And it doesn't hurt to develop general familiarity with tech.

In any case, our emphasis should be on learning how we learn best. And the more you learn about any of those things I mentioned out of your own curiosity, the better the position you'll be in to adapt to the changes the future brings. Not only to your job, because the specific things you learn may never directly apply to your job at all—but they'll help you adapt to everything that is changing in the world around you.

Chapter 25:

How to predict the future (through a Strategic Optimist lens)

THINKING ABOUT THE FUTURE IS a particular kind of skill. We all have it: Every one of us thinks about the future at some level of specificity all the time. Otherwise we'd never make plans.

But pondering whether to meet up with friends or go to a movie on Friday night isn't as complicated as predicting what the major drivers of business and the economy will be in three-to-five years. Aside from the larger time horizon, you're looking at more moving parts, more unknowns—and more consequences to getting it wrong. So sure, there's a pretty sizeable advantage to developing skill in making predictions and forecasts.

"The future cannot be predicted, but futures can be invented."

—**Dennis Gabor**, *Inventing the Future*[236]

For reasons I have tried to make clear, *predicting* the future isn't always the most meaningful activity even when it comes to thinking about the future. But there are indeed times when it does come in handy to be able to forecast—to draw dotted lines from the past through the present and see where they seem to lead.

I should pause to add a semantic note here as a public service to humanity: Let's agree that there's a difference between predictions and trends. One of my pet peeves is that around the end of every year, we drown in a deluge of " trends" articles, blog posts, and reports that pertain to the year *ahead*.

The new year doesn't have trends yet. What the post is doing is either looking at *trends* observed throughout the previous year, or making *predictions* about the upcoming year, or some combination of both. You can even predict what the trends will be, but you can't report on trends that haven't happened yet.

And more than a personal annoyance, it's actually a meaningful distinction. Those of us who live in the liminal space between strategy and futurism spend an awful lot of time and energy monitoring trends. We like to have a sense of what people are buying, what they're wearing, what they're eating, how they're talking, and so on. All of this helps us envision trajectories. If you've been paying attention to food and drink trends, for example, you know that (as of this writing) plant-based foods are growing in popularity. (And that certainly won't surprise you after the A Brighter Future for How and What We Eat chapter.) So are nonalcoholic beverages. Either trend is somewhat interesting in itself, but taken together, do they suggest other subcategories of food and drink that could be the next thing? *That's* where the prediction starts.

---

[236] Dennis Gabor in his 1963 book "Inventing the Future."[1]
He was later awarded a Nobel Prize in Physics for his work in holography.

Gabor, Dennis, Inventing the future, 1963, Secker and Warburg, London, pp.184-185 according to https://quoteinvestigator.com/2012/09/27/invent-the-future/

Why do we need to know the next thing? "The market will reward us for it if we're right" is one answer, and there's nothing incorrect about that. It's the economic reality. But more fundamentally, and more to the point of Strategic Optimism, by using our skills of prediction and forecasting well, we will learn about what matters and what is going to matter. We will learn how to align our efforts with what will resonate, and how to frame our work so it will bring people along. We will learn what the emerging Change Factors are likely to be. Our empathy will allow us to see how various people are (and will be) affected by the changes. We will begin to see bold ways forward.

So with that in mind, the following section is by no means an exhaustive reference on forecasting and prediction—you can find plenty of additional resources by searching your favorite search engine or bookstore—but in the context of Strategic Optimism, here are some skills you can sharpen that will help you see more clearly.

Read and consume media widely. Don't limit your sources to those you agree with.

There's no substitute for getting a real feel from across political views, highbrow and lowbrow, across the range of people's influences. Read or listen to books for depth, follow social media accounts for breadth, take in a range of podcasts, watch movies and documentaries from outside your usual taste, and so on.

After all, a Strategic Optimist needs to understand a wide swath of perspectives to continually try to create the best futures for the most people.

Develop your radar for cultural strategy.

Pay attention to the hints and cues in entertainment, advertising, media, and everyday dialogue of people's attitudes and values about health, wealth, success, work, love, relationships, sex, family, home, etc.

As an added perk, this gives you the advantage of greater cultural relevance. If you are creating intellectual property, such as a book (ahem), and you want it to land with resonance and be able to straddle that dual need of timeless and timely, it helps to think about the context it'll be arriving in. If you're launching a product, you need to know what else is happening in the cultural landscape that will help determine its success.

Articulate what you think the trends are. Keep an actual list.

Sometimes you'll see some of the same themes popping up in news stories and in the general discourse on social media and in your environment. Perhaps you've noticed, for example, the trend toward gender fluidity and post-gender expression. That's interesting and could inform the way products are developed and marketed, so we'd want to write that down.

Look for through-lines from the past through the present.

Even the weirdest and wildest innovations, like gene editing, usually have precedents somewhere, or maybe multiple somewheres. Look backward from the items and issues that have caught your attention to see where they came from, what collection of sources and cultural touchpoints influenced them. The better you get at tracing the paths of these trajectories, the better you'll be able to envision these kinds of arcs forward for emerging products and topics, and not just backward.

The great "data versus your gut" debate isn't settled.

Chances are, if you ask a group of data analysts whether they trust data or their gut, 90-ish percent of them will say data. And if you ask a group of executives whether they trust data or their gut, 90-ish percent of them will say their gut.

Both answers are right and both are wrong. Hey look, it's our old friend both/and!

There's a blurry line between allowing your bias to override objective data and not letting context-free numbers obscure what's clearer to your human senses. You have to learn to ride that line a bit.

As Nate Silver writes in *The Signal and the Noise*:

> "The forecasters know the flaws in the computer models.
> [...] These are the sorts of distinctions that forecasters glean

over time as they learn to work around the flaws in the model, in the way that a skilled pool player can adjust to the dead spots on the table at his local bar. [...]

The unique resource that these forecasters were contributing was their eyesight. It is a valuable tool for forecasters in any discipline—a visual inspection of a graphic showing the interaction between two variables is often a quicker and more reliable way to detect outliers in your data than a statistical test. It's also one of those areas where computers lag well behind the human brain."

It makes sense, after all. Meaning is our core Human Superpower, and making things make sense is what meaning does. Our senses like sight, sound, touch, etc., appropriately enough, are part of how we make sense.

Machines can crunch numbers far faster and more accurately than we humans can, but humans are able to bring a great deal of nuanced perception from our sensory input. So when you use spreadsheets and databases and machine learning to process data sets, have a specific question you're looking for an answer to, if you like, but let your human instinct have a say too.

Reflect but don't ruminate.

Rumination on its own can go in circles; the best insights tend to occur during rest cycles between efforts of researching and attempting to write new thoughts.

Try to connect dots, and imagine what is going to matter.

Remember that everything is connected, so try to see what happens when you think about one trend you've observed in the context of another. What opportunities does that juxtaposition create? Remember that innovation is about *what is going to matter*. What can you see beginning to matter in the context of the emerging trend landscape you're noting?

Make guesses, and keep track of them.

Insights, of course, are valuable, and they can make or break strategic clarity. But for planning, the real trick is foresight. You don't have to publish your guesses, but write them down for yourself, at least. Start to notice whether you got them directionally right but subtly wrong, or if you had the right idea but the time horizon was off.

When you learn to think about it this way, the future fills with possibilities. Good luck, and I can't wait to see the future you help lead us into.

POSTSCRIPT:

The Strategic Optimist's Manifesto

This last part is a "manifesto"-style summary of the ideas in this book.
You can cut or even tear these pages out and hang them on your wall,
give them to someone who needs to see them,
or just refer back to them when you need a reminder.

The Strategic Optimist's Manifesto

(OR: EVERYTHING IS CONNECTED, REDUX)

The future of human experience is deeply integrated; everything depends on everything else. Our fates are interlinked. So although over the last decade I have characterized my career as "helping humanity prepare for an increasingly tech-driven future," I now believe humanity has to prepare for the tech-driven future at scale by preparing for and mitigating everything else at scale: climate catastrophe; the cyclical expansion and collapse of globalization; ongoing geopolitical conflict; financial market upheaval; the legacy of racism, slavery, and colonialism; algorithmically-enhanced culture wars; the decline of trust; extreme wealth inequity and widespread poverty; etc. But everything is too connected to treat one challenge as if it exists in a vacuum, far from the influence of the others.

We also need to prepare for this future in a way that respects the human scale of life, experiences, well-being, and rights—all without jeopardizing the natural ecosystem, nonhuman animals, or the potential for future life to flourish. In fact, part of the work that lies ahead of us is to move our way of life toward a more harmonious and respectful relationship with the natural world.

With all the change we face that is threatening or at least alarming, we owe it to ourselves and to the generations still ahead of us to look for the brightest possible outcomes and work diligently toward them.

Nothing short of our full commitment to an optimistic view will do.

For this view to work, we will have to shake off the cynicism of dystopian defaults and instead use integrative thinking and Strategic Optimism to develop a unifying framework for what an inclusive, connected better future for all looks like; create new curricula that includes early education on AI and the implications of algorithmic bias; identify new measures and standards of success, and more.

Envision bold new ways forward

and then commit to those bold ideas.

This way forward, Strategic Optimism, is rooted in what makes humanity thrive:

An understanding of meaning—that meaning is the central human condition, meaning-making and meaning-seeking, that we thrive on meaning, and that at every level, meaning is about what matters.

And the further understanding that innovation, then, is about what is going to matter. And we need to let that meaning-centered—and therefore human-centered—approach to innovation lead our development of emerging technology and data-driven experiences.

This approach will need to be built around exponential change in multiple areas, including artificial intelligence, workplace automation, the climate crisis, and more. And it must work alongside existing unifying frameworks for improvement of life on a global scale, such as the Sustainable Development Goals from the United Nations. Those seventeen goals themselves interconnect in important ways; ending poverty in all its forms everywhere (SDG #1) and ensuring inclusive and equitable quality education for all (SDG #4) are listed as separate goals, but they're likely to be related both in approach and in results.

And we do want to move "forward"

So often when change disrupts us, we talk about how we can't wait to get "back to normal" or "back" to the way things were. But the only direction that works is forward. Backward is not a direction consistent with living. It's understandable, especially when we feel a sense of loss or grief over what we used to have. While we need to honor our grief and allow ourselves to heal, we ultimately need our energy focused not on going back to what we feel we lost, but going forward into the future as it could be.

Remember: We spend a lot of time thinking about what could go wrong and not nearly enough time imagining and planning for what we want to go right. But also remember the power in the kind of integrative thinking that allows us to see both/and: We can integrate all of our thinking, acknowledge all the possibilities of what's going on around us, acknowledge the reality of what's happening, and acknowledge the full range of possible outcomes out of any given thing that happens to us. But then choose the direction of action.

We can use hope as a tool of *focus and refocus*. Whenever things change, whenever anything happens around us, we have the opportunity to choose where we'll put our energy, our focus, our time, and our attention. But whatever we hope for, we are also compelling ourselves to work for. Optimism obligates us. Optimism isn't about seeing only the good; it's about committing to the good we see as we look ahead. Wherever we can see a better way forward, we have a responsibility to work toward it.

An optimistic view of the future can allow us to envision bold new ways forward.

An optimistic view of the future implies that we have a responsibility to work toward better outcomes.

> **But optimism alone won't bring about the best outcomes.**
>
> **Optimism needs a strategy,**
>
> **and hope needs action.**

Build from the Strategic Optimism Model

First, identify the **Change Factors** that lie ahead of you.

Then:

1. **Be honest** about the fullness of the situation, even if it initially looks bleak.
2. **Recognize** what matters (this is *meaning*!)
3. **Identify** what is going to matter (this is where *innovation* comes in!)
4. **Go all in on hope** as a tool of focus and refocus
5. **Habituate** to change (meaning: get used to it!)
6. **Tune in with empathy** to anticipate what needs to change
7. **Envision bold** ways forward
8. **Resolve to work** toward the best futures for the most people

Use your Human Superpowers

Both/and: moving beyond dystopia versus utopia and thinking about the future in an integrative, holistic way that resists reductive thinking and accepts the power of inherent contrasts and contradictions

Courage: our capacity to hope, to resist cynicism, and to lead others bravely toward our optimistic vision with strategy and purpose

Empathy and adaptation: the predictive instinct for how people will be affected, and the reactive ability to respond and change

Collaboration and teamwork: our ability to put aside our individual differences and our self-interest, and band with others to achieve greater outcomes—another way of saying collective action, which is a recurring theme throughout the applied approaches to the brighter future

And most of all:

Meaning: the core Human Superpower that gives us all insight into what matters

This is the beginning, not the end.

While we work collectively on this new view and broader framework, we can start by adding a new decision checklist to our workflow when we introduce new experiences, new products, new interactions, new modalities of communication, etc.

1. To ground our decisions in a meaning-oriented view of human experience, we must ask "What *matters*?"

2. To focus our innovative efforts on the meaningful future for humanity, we must ask, "What is *going to matter*?"

3. We need to consider these questions at *both* the human, individual scale *and* at the scale of society and humanity.

4. We must consider the *impact* they may have.

5. And we must consider these questions across a wide range of areas such as the SDGs, across systems, with explicit acknowledgement of the interconnectedness of all things.

We *must* make decisions so they will make the best futures. This is not about slowing down innovation (although sometimes a little slowness can be a gift); it's about making our contributions more thoughtful, more aligned, and more meaningful. It's about helping us innovate what is going to matter. It's not about avoiding dystopia or creating utopia. It's about making something we choose, intentionally, with clarity and purpose.

I'm excited to see how we all tackle the Change Factors we face now that we have Strategic Optimism and we know our own Human Superpowers. That's what I hope this book can do for all of us: help us prepare for change and use our Human Superpowers to create the best futures for the most people.

No matter what challenge you face, you can apply some or all of the tools of Strategic Optimism to determine the best way forward.

More than anything, we must proceed from the understanding that we want to be on the right side of history.

The summary is the same as the starting point: Inclusion. Connectedness. Humanity. Hope.

There are many possible futures, but a brighter future demands relentlessly optimistic and radically strategic collective action toward the best possible futures for the most people possible.

The future is less one than it is many.

We are less many than we are one.

Everything, everything, everything is connected.

Gratitude

Thanks to: Jocelyn Bailey for her intrepid editorial work and always saying yes to taking on my projects, no matter how ambitious the concept or timeline; the team at Interrobang for their dual roles chasing down research and offering thoughtful design; Elizabeth Marshall for her invaluable counsel; all of my incredible guests on The Tech Humanist Show whose interviews were rich with insights; Jennifer Iannolo who has been my go-to person for strategic feedback on every aspect of my work, and all the other brilliant and accomplished friends who have offered clarifying feedback on every piece of the concept; the clients, speaking bureaus, and supporters who have seen the value in this book idea and championed it from the beginning; and to Robbie Quinn, who not only takes the best portrait photos anyone could ever ask for but who was patient with me while I worked on this book during the darkest days of the pandemic (even as he was working on his own book), and who has encouraged, supported, and loved me for my insistence on seeing the bright side.

About the Author

Kate O'Neill helps leaders create meaningful human experiences in a tech-driven world and take responsibility for the future we all share. She is founder and CEO of KO Insights, a strategic advisory firm providing big-picture thinking on how business, humanity, and technology interact at scale, and committed to improving human experience amid exponential change.

Among her prior highlights, she was one of the first 100 employees at Netflix and created the first content management role there; she developed Toshiba America's first intranet; and founded [meta]marketer, a first-of-its-kind digital strategy and analytics agency.

Kate is widely known as the "Tech Humanist," which is also the title of her most recent previous book and the namesake of her live interview show. As a renowned technologist, writer, speaker, and ethicist, Kate regularly keynotes industry events, advocating for the best futures for humanity in an increasingly tech-driven and exponentially-changing world. Clients and audiences have included Google, Yale University, the city of Amsterdam, and the United Nations. Her insights have been featured in WIRED and many other outlets, and she has appeared as an expert tech commentator on BBC and a wide variety of international media.

Kate is on a mission to help people prepare for an increasingly tech-driven world and for change at exponential scale with her signature strategic optimism. (She has rarely been seen without sunglasses on top of her head. Her favorite pairs are from Parafina, a brand that makes sunglasses from recycled materials like tires, & HDPE, & PET plastic, and is a B-Corp that donates 5% of their income to giving kids access to primary school supplies in Paraguay.)

More information about Kate, including ways to connect, can be found at:

http://www.koinsights.com/about/about-kate-oneill/

Made in the USA
Columbia, SC
01 October 2021